200
DEMANDING
CHESS
PUZZLES

200
DEMANDING
CHESS
PUZZLES

**Edited
by
Martin Greif**

Sterling Publishing Co., Inc. New York

Library of Congress Cataloging-in-Publication Data Available

10 9 8 7 6 5 4 3 2 1

Published by Sterling Publishing Company, Inc.
387 Park Avenue South, New York, N.Y. 10016
© 1996 by Sterling Publishing Company, Inc.
Distributed in Canada by Sterling Publishing
C/o Canadian Manda Group, One Atlantic Avenue, Suite 105
Toronto, Ontario, Canada M6K 3E7
Distributed in Great Britain and Europe by Cassell PLC
Wellington House, 125 Strand, London WC2R 0BB, England
Distributed in Australia by Capricorn Link (Australia) Pty Ltd.
P.O. Box 6651, Baulkham Hills, Business Centre, NSW 2153, Australia
Manufactured in the United States of America

ISBN 0-8069-5977-0

CONTENTS

INTRODUCTION

Through the years chess has had an expansive literature, with virtually every element of the game anatomized in depth. Oddly, very few collections of classic chess problems have been published, an oversight corrected by publication of *200 Classic Chess Puzzles* (Sterling Publishing Company, 1993) and *200 Challenging Chess Puzzles* (Sterling Publishing Company, 1995). The popular reception of these two anthologies has generated requests for a third collection of brain-teasing chess problems, a wish satisfied by publication of the present book.

The object in chess, of course, is to trap, or checkmate, the opponent's King into a check from which it cannot escape, thus bringing the game to a victorious conclusion. *200 Demanding Chess Puzzles* is a collection of gripping, grueling, and teeth-grating end games in which a checkmate, or mate, is required in two, three, four, or more moves. Shown the illustration of a board with chess pieces in fixed positions, it's up to you to determine how to take the King in a given number of moves. What's more, if you're to solve the puzzle successfully, you have to take the part of both players, seeing the game from the point of view of both Black and White. In these riveting chess puzzles, you'll be forced to play the end game both aggressively and defensively, keeping the pieces of both opponents concentrated in logical cooperation until you can say with certainty, "the King is dead," the literal meaning of the Persian *shah mat*, from which the term "checkmate" derives.

200 Demanding Chess Puzzles is intended for both the player with only an elementary understanding of the game and for the more advanced player who wishes to test his skill. Since the end game is the most important phase of chess, and a good end-game player can vanquish the opening or middle-game specialist, concentrating on these brilliant puzzles will not only provide hours of brain-teasing fun, but may help you to be a better end-game player and enable you to enjoy the challenging endings and therefore chess to the full. Included in the puzzles are Pawn endings, Queen endings, Queen and Pawn endings, Rook and Pawn endings, and minor piece endings. *200 Demanding Chess Puzzles*, all culled from award-winning chess problems from the past, forces you to play end games that are full of excitement, color, brilliance, and subtlety. And, if you're stumped, or even if you're not, the solutions appear in the back of the book.

A word or two about these solutions is in order. First, the shorthand used to describe chess play in these pages is a modified form of standard Descriptive (or English) Notation, with a dash (—) indicating moves (e.g. P—K4) and an *x* indicating captures (e.g. Q x B). Such abbreviations as *ch*, *db ch*, and *dis ch* (check, double check, and discovers [reveals] check) are obvious, while the beginner may, perhaps, need to be reminded that *e.p.* stands for a capture *en passant*.

Second, since many of the puzzles allow for *more* than one solution, alternative solutions — frequently more than one — are offered. These alternative solutions and moves are indicated by asterisks (*, **, or ***).

Finally, several of the puzzles are not only tricky in their own right, but tricky by design — that is, while the correct solution might call for, say, four moves, you might in fact give mate in only three. The challenge lies in finding the *stipulated* number of moves, even if there is an easier way! With this caveat in mind, enjoy these 200 classic chess challenges to the full.

PUZZLES

PUZZLE No. 1
Black

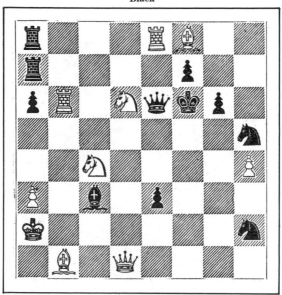

White
White to play and mate in three moves.

PUZZLE No. 2
Black

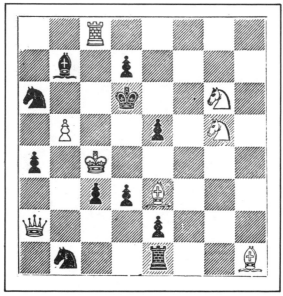

White
White to play and mate in four moves.

PUZZLE No. 3
Black

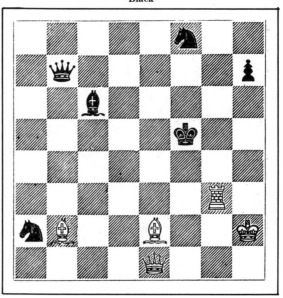

White
White to play and mate in three moves.

PUZZLE No. 4
Black

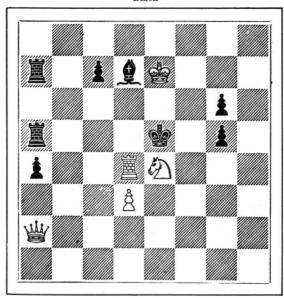

White
White to play and mate in four moves.

PUZZLE No. 5
Black

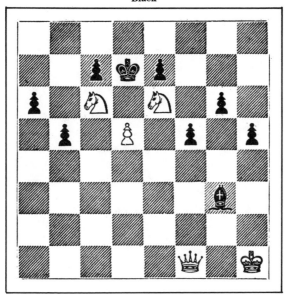

White
White to play and mate in four moves.

PUZZLE No. 6
Black

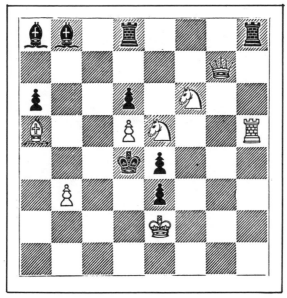

White
White to play and mate in three moves.

PUZZLE No. 7
Black

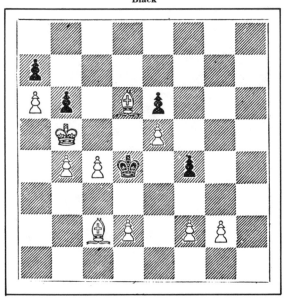

White
White to play and mate in five moves.

PUZZLE No. 8
Black

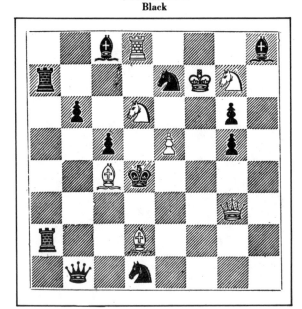

White
White to play and mate in five moves.

14

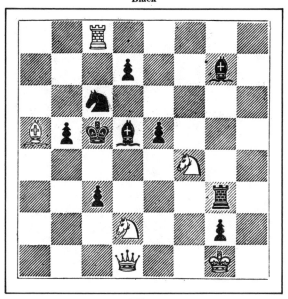

White
White to play and mate in four moves.

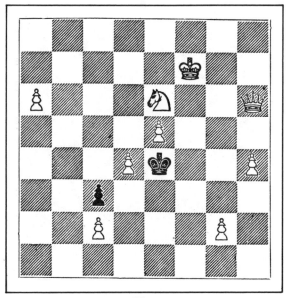

White
White to play and mate in three moves.

PUZZLE No. 11
Black

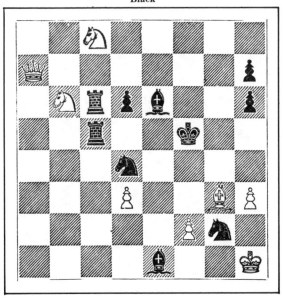

White
White to play and mate in five moves.

PUZZLE No. 12
Black

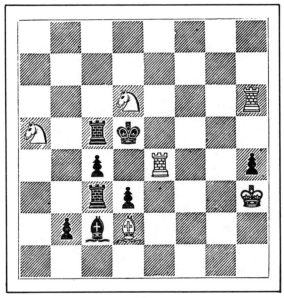

White
White to play and mate in four moves.

16

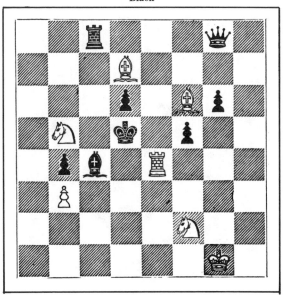

White
White to play and mate in four moves.

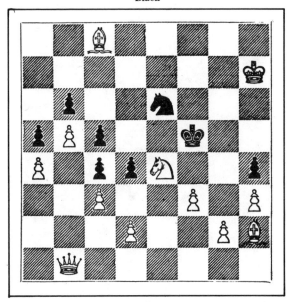

White
White to play and mate in three moves.

PUZZLE No. 15
Black

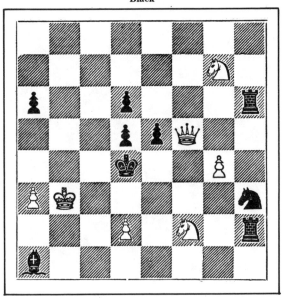

White
White to play and mate in four moves.

PUZZLE No. 16
Black

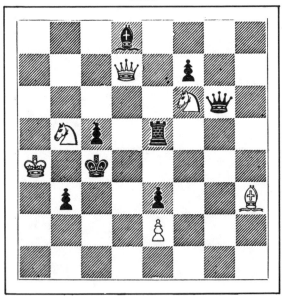

White
White to play and mate in three moves.

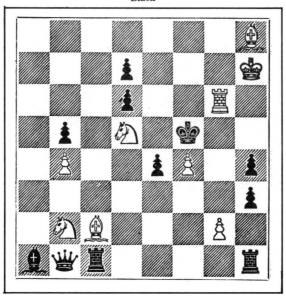

White
White to play and mate in five moves.

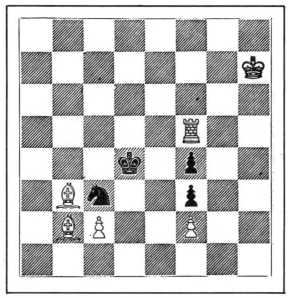

White
White to play and mate in three moves.

PUZZLE No. 19
Black

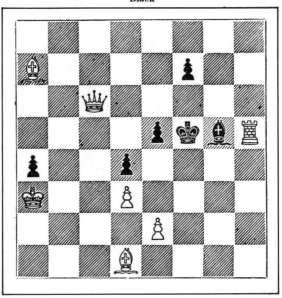

White
White to play and mate in three moves.

PUZZLE No. 20
Black

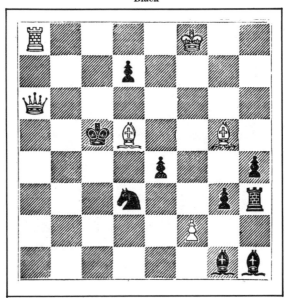

White
White to play and mate in three moves.

PUZZLE No. 21
Black

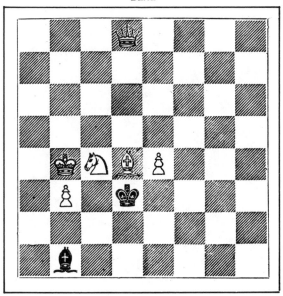

White
White to play and mate in four moves.

PUZZLE No. 22
Black

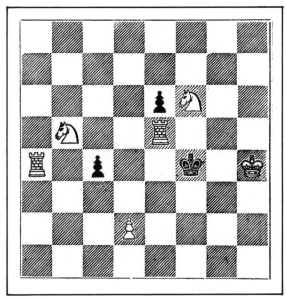

White
White to play and mate in three moves.

White
White to play and mate in three moves.

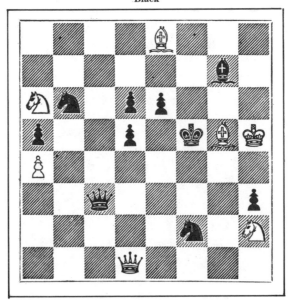

White
White to play and mate in four moves.

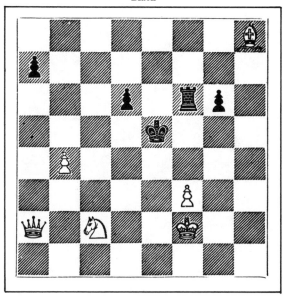

White
White to play and mate in three moves.

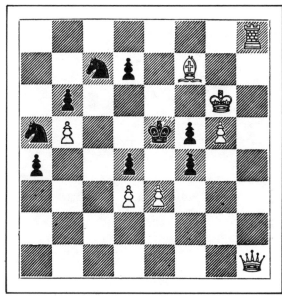

White
White to play and mate in five moves.

PUZZLE No. 27
Black

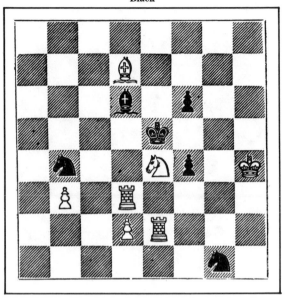

White
White or Black to play and mate in four moves.

PUZZLE No. 28
Black

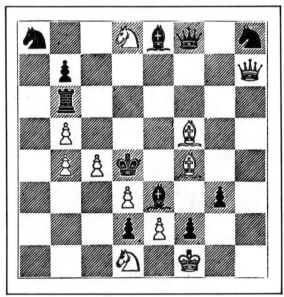

White
White to play and mate in five moves.

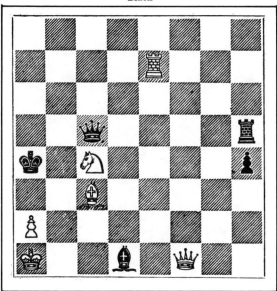

White
White to play and mate in four moves.

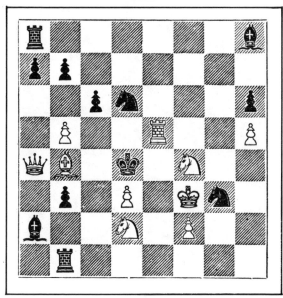

White
White to play and mate in four moves.

PUZZLE No. 31
Black

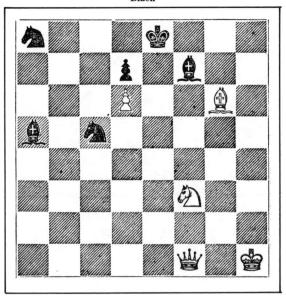

White
White to play and mate in three moves.

PUZZLE No. 32
Black

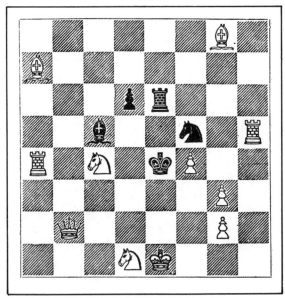

White
White to play and mate in two moves.

PUZZLE No. 33
Black

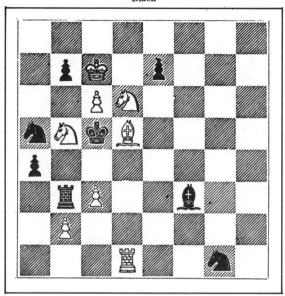

White
White to play and mate in three moves.

PUZZLE No. 34
Black

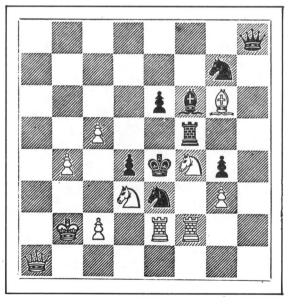

White
White to play and mate in three moves.

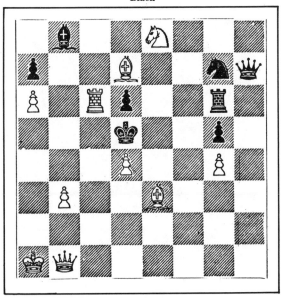

White
White to play and mate in three moves.

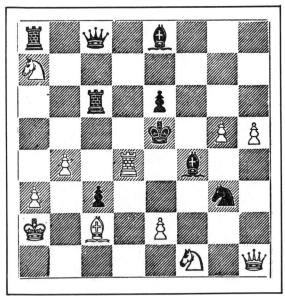

White
White to play and mate in four moves.

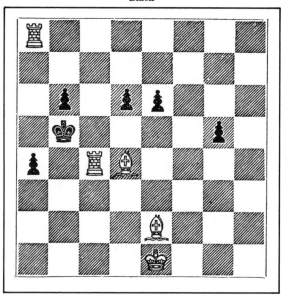

White
White to play and mate in three moves.

White
White to play and mate in four moves.

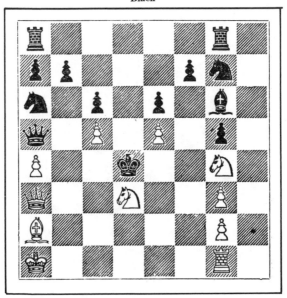

White
White to play and mate in four moves.

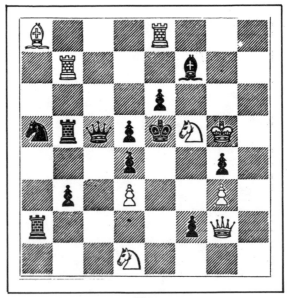

White
White to play and mate in four moves.

PUZZLE No. 41
Black

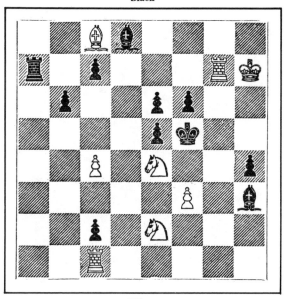

White
White to play and mate in four moves.

PUZZLE No. 42
Black

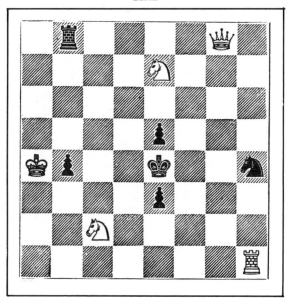

White
White to play and mate in four moves.

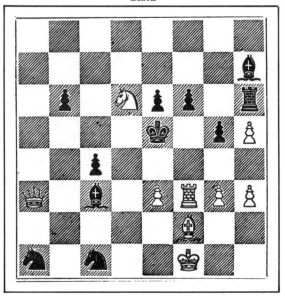

White
White to play and mate in four moves.

White
White to play and mate in four moves.

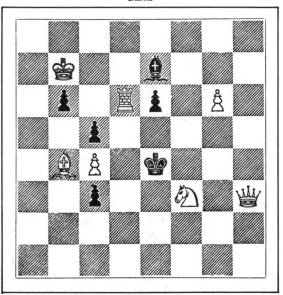

White
White to play and mate in three moves.

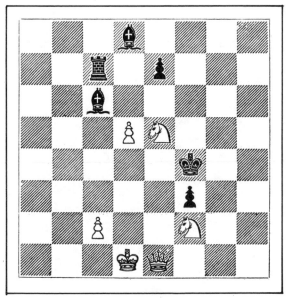

White
White to play and mate in three moves.

PUZZLE No. 47
Black

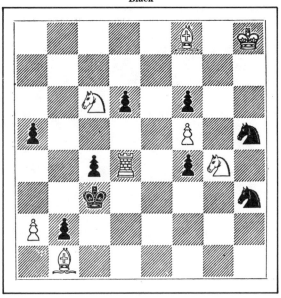

White
White to play and mate in three moves.

PUZZLE No. 48
Black

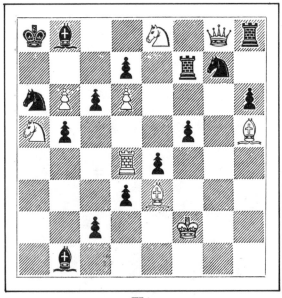

White
White to play and mate in three moves.

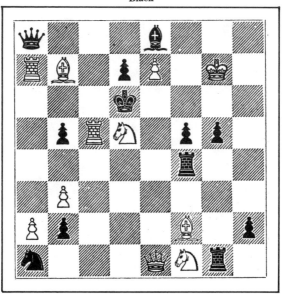

White
White to play and mate in three moves.

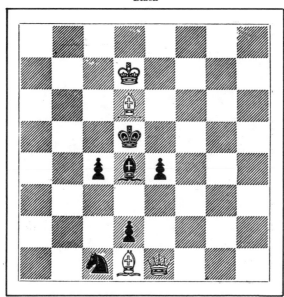

White
White to play and mate in three moves.

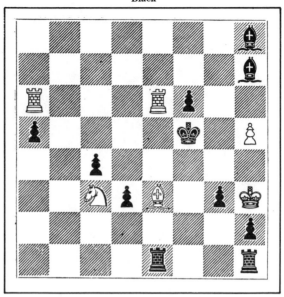

White
White to play and mate in four moves.

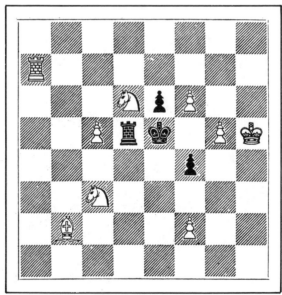

White
White to play and mate in four moves.

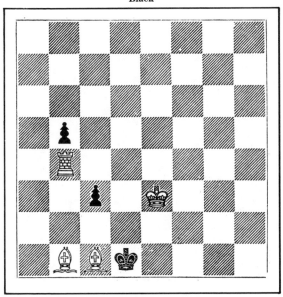

White
White to play and mate in four moves.

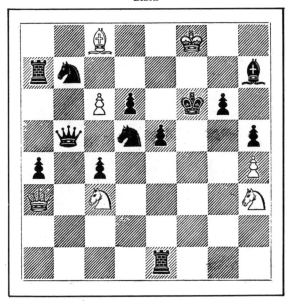

White
White to play and mate in four moves.

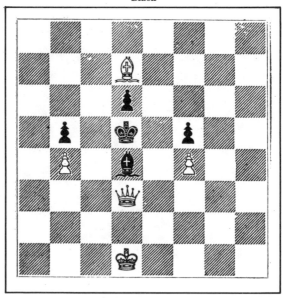

White
White to play and mate in four moves.

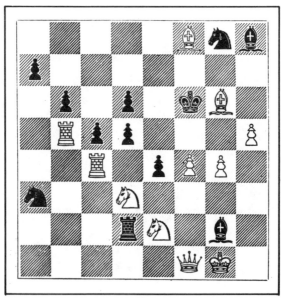

White
White to play and mate in five moves.

PUZZLE No. 57
Black

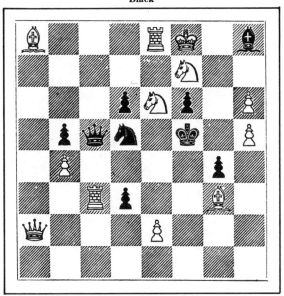

White
White to play and mate in two moves.

PUZZLE No. 58
Black

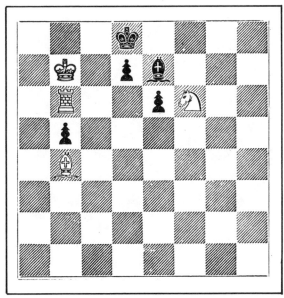

White
White to play and mate in two moves.

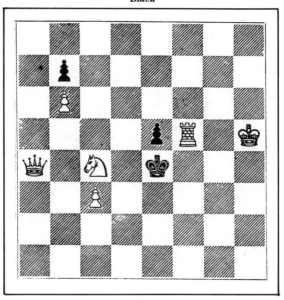

White to play and mate in three moves.

PUZZLE No. 60
Black

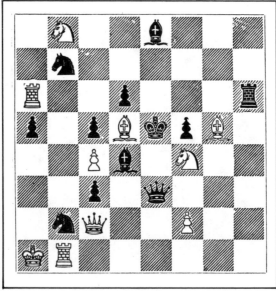

White
White to play and mate in three moves.

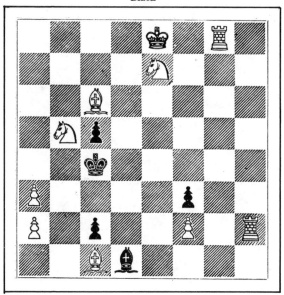

White
White to play and mate in three moves.

White
White to play and mate in four moves.

PUZZLE No. 63
Black

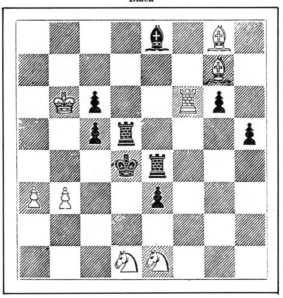

White
White to play and mate in three moves.

PUZZLE No. 64
Black

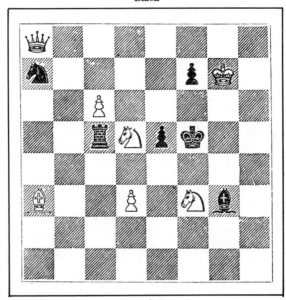

White
White to play and mate in three moves.

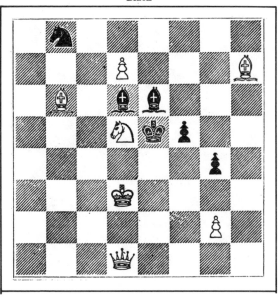

White
White to play and mate in three moves.

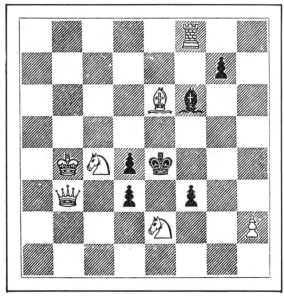

White
White to play and mate in three moves.

White
White to play and mate in three moves.

PUZZLE No. 68
Black

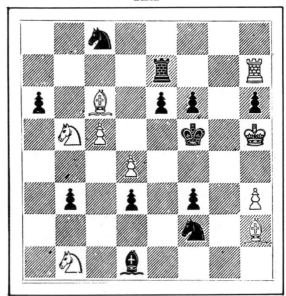

White
White to play and mate in four moves.

44

PUZZLE No. 69
Black

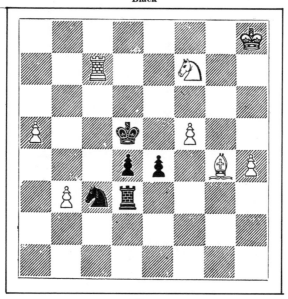

White
White to play and mate in four moves.

PUZZLE No. 70
Black

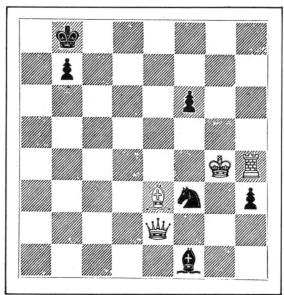

White
White to play and mate in three moves.

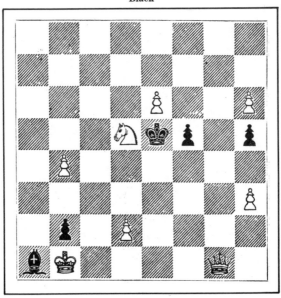

White
White to play and mate in three moves.

PUZZLE No. 72
Black

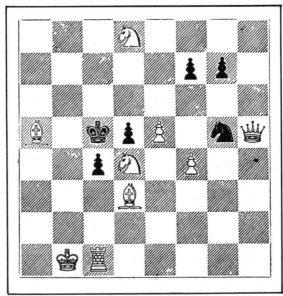

White
White to play and mate in three moves.

46

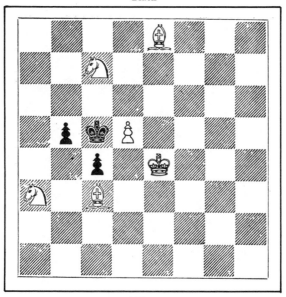

White
White to play and mate in three moves.

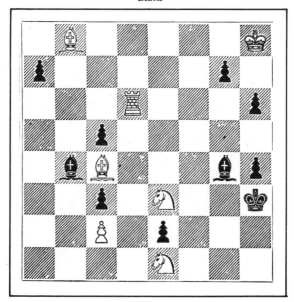

White
White to play and mate in three moves.

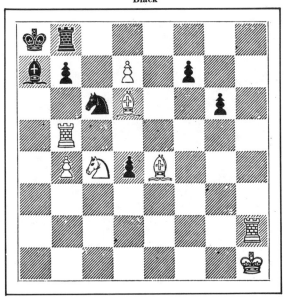

White
White to play and mate in four moves.

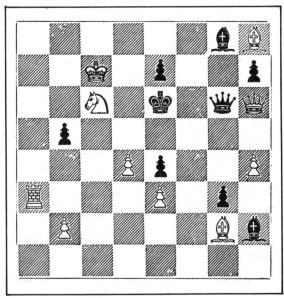

White
White to play and mate in four moves.

PUZZLE No. 77
Black

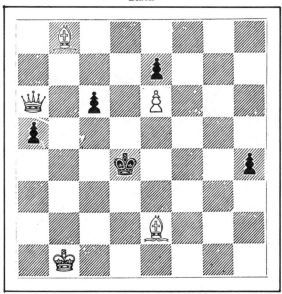

White
White to play and mate in three moves.

PUZZLE No. 78
Black

White
White to play and mate in three moves.

49

White
White to play and mate in two moves.

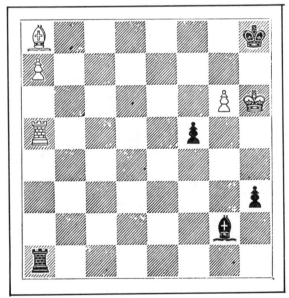

White
White to play and mate in three moves.

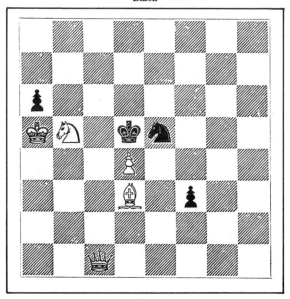

White
White to play and mate in three moves.

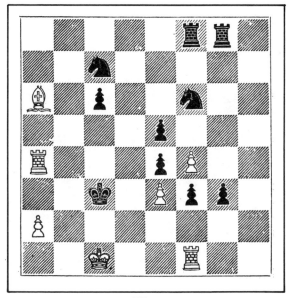

White
White to play and mate in three moves.

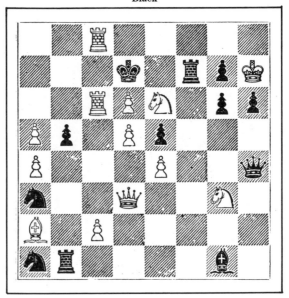

White
White to play and mate in four moves.

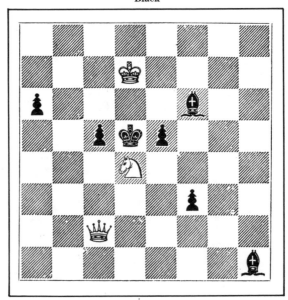

White
White to play and mate in three moves.

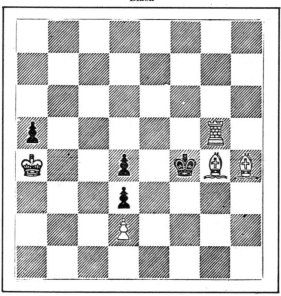

White
White to play and mate in four moves.

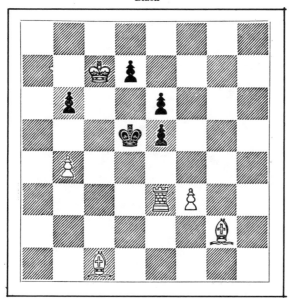

White
White to play and mate in four moves.

PUZZLE No. 87
Black

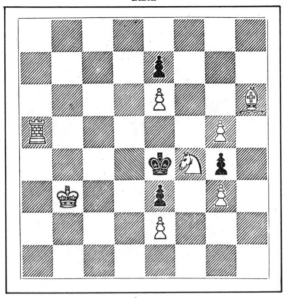

White
White to play and mate in four moves.

PUZZLE No. 88
Black

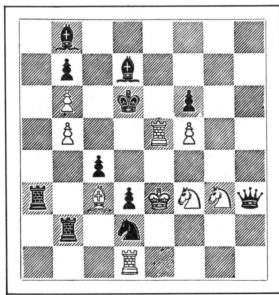

White
White to play and draw the game.

PUZZLE No. 89
Black

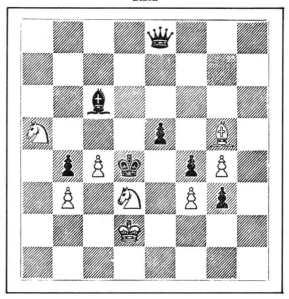

White
White to play and mate in five moves.

PUZZLE No. 90
Black

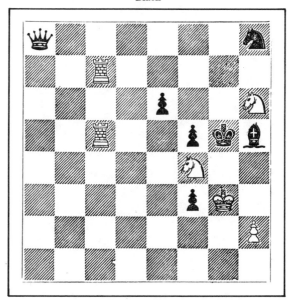

White
White to play and mate in four moves.

55

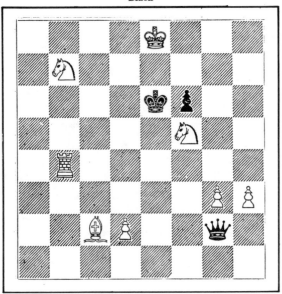

White
White to play and mate in five moves.

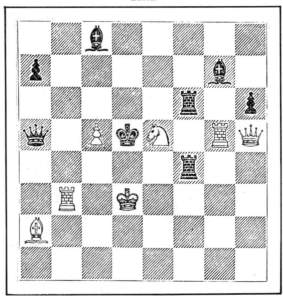

White
White to play and mate in four moves.

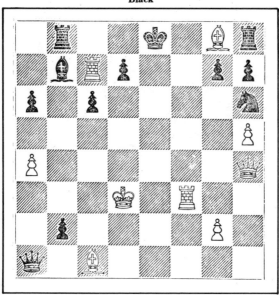

White
White to play and mate in five moves.

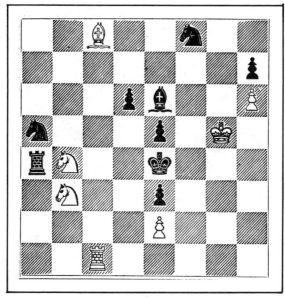

White
White to play and mate in three moves.

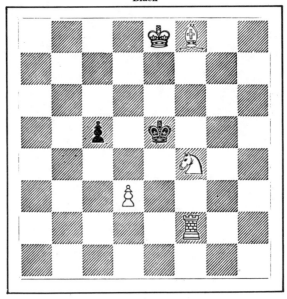

White
White to play and mate in six moves.

White
White to play and mate in four moves.

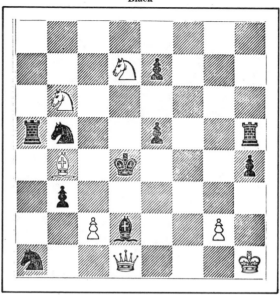

White
White to play and mate in three moves.

White
White to play and mate in five moves.

White
White to play and mate in three moves.

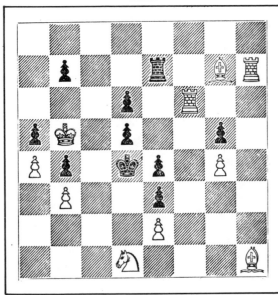

White
White to play and mate in four moves.

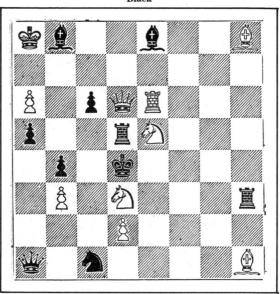

White
White to play and mate in four moves.

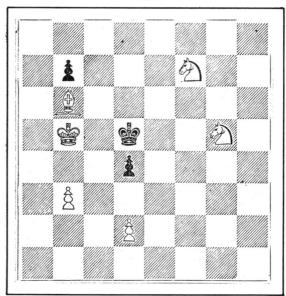

White
White to play and mate in four moves.

White
White to play and mate in five moves.

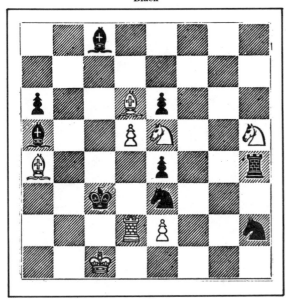

White
White to play and mate in four moves.

PUZZLE No. 105
Black

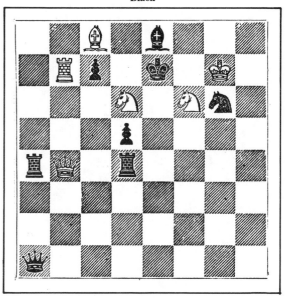

White
White to play and mate in three moves.

PUZZLE No. 106
Black

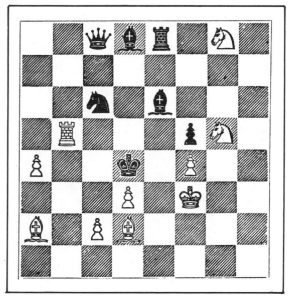

White
White to play and mate in five moves.

PUZZLE No. 107
Black

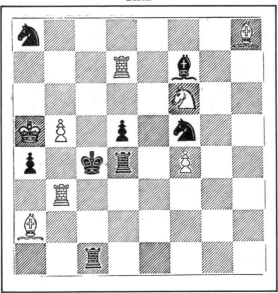

White
White to play and mate in four moves.

PUZZLE No. 108
Black

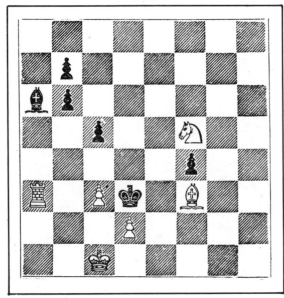

White
White to play and mate in three moves.

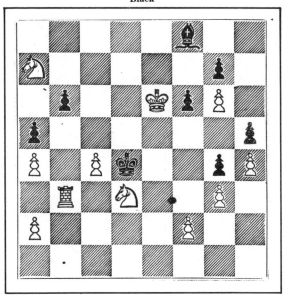

White
White to play and mate in four moves.

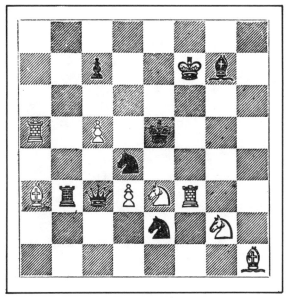

White
White to play and mate in three moves.

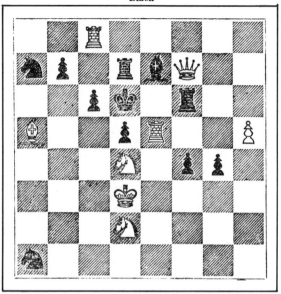

White
White to play and mate in three moves.

PUZZLE No. 112
Black

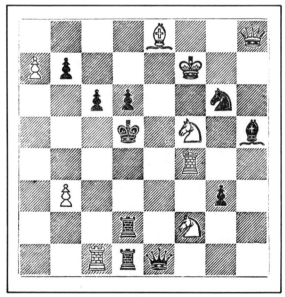

White
White to play and mate in six moves.

White
White to play and mate in three moves.

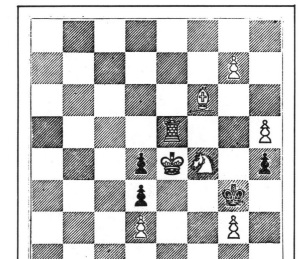

White
White to play and mate in four moves.

PUZZLE No. 117
Black

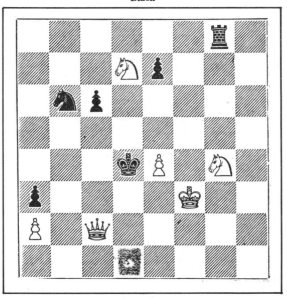

White
White to play and mate in four moves.

PUZZLE No. 118
Black

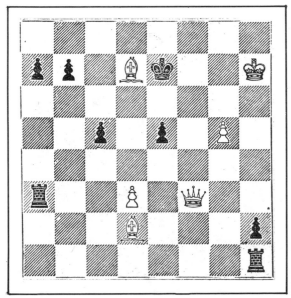

White
White to play and mate in three moves.

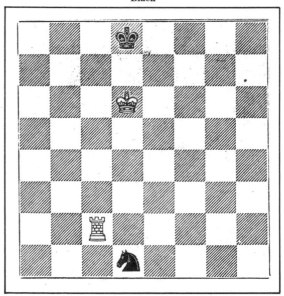

White
White to play and mate in three moves.

White
White to play and mate in four moves.

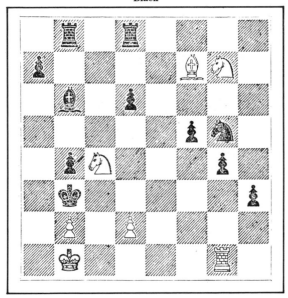

White
White to play and mate in six moves.

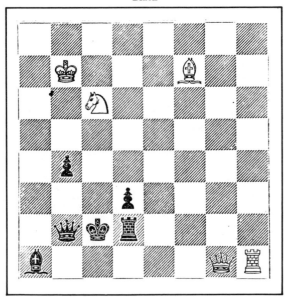

White
White to play and mate in three moves.

PUZZLE No. 121
Black

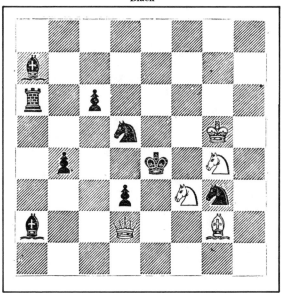

White
White to play and mate in three moves.

PUZZLE No. 122
Black

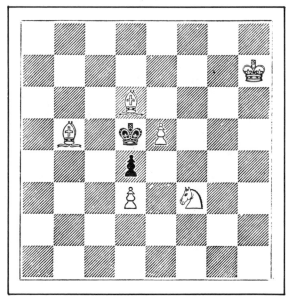

White
White to play and mate in three moves.

PUZZLE No. 123
Black

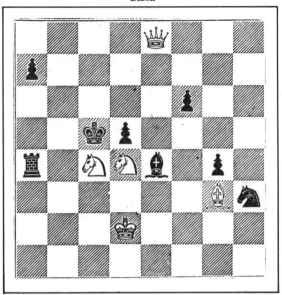

White
White to play and mate in three moves.

PUZZLE No. 124
Black

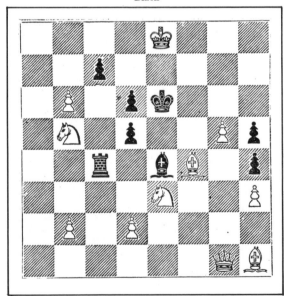

White
White to play and mate in three moves.

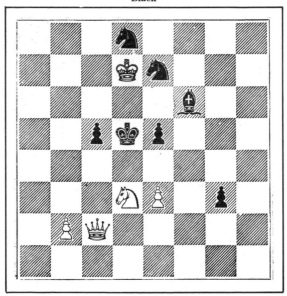

White
White to play and mate in five moves.

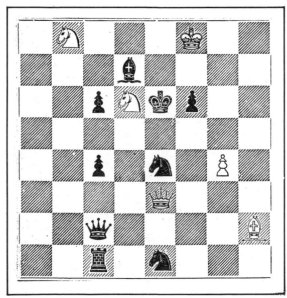

White
White to play and mate in four moves.

73

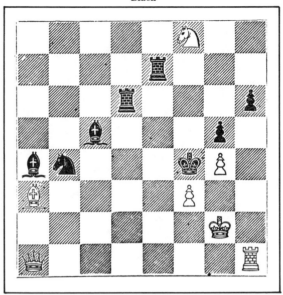

White
White to play and mate in five moves.

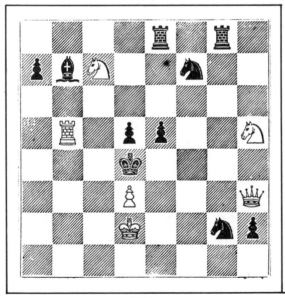

White
White to play and mate in four moves.

White
White to play and mate in three moves.

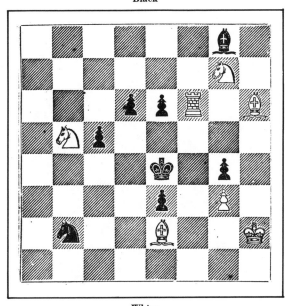

White
White to play and mate in five moves.

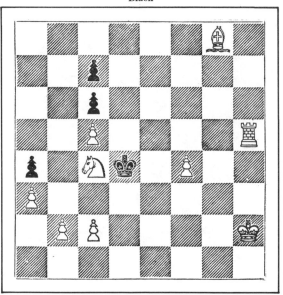

White
White to play and mate in four moves.

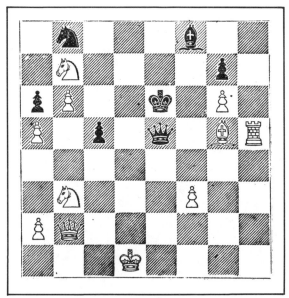

White
White to play and mate in five moves.

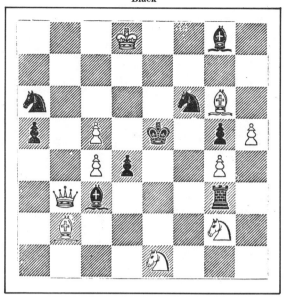

White
White to play and mate in four moves.

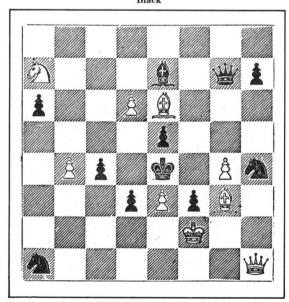

White
White to play and mate in four moves.

PUZZLE No. 135
Black

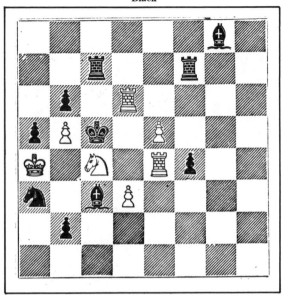

White
White to play and mate in three moves.

PUZZLE No. 136
Black

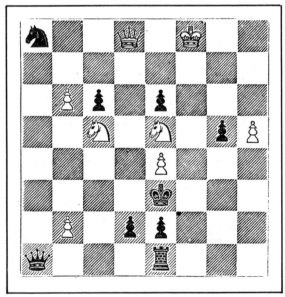

White
White to play and mate in four moves.

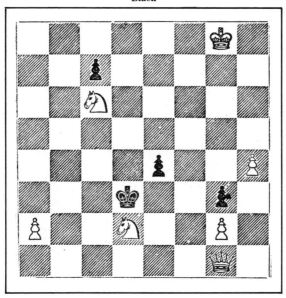

White
White to play and mate in four moves.

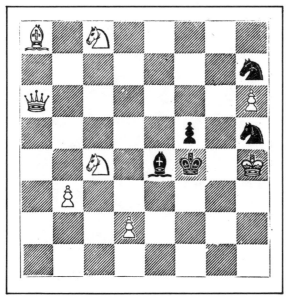

White
White to play and mate in three moves.

PUZZLE No. 139
Black

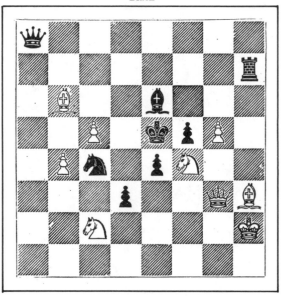

White
White to play and mate in four moves.

PUZZLE No. 140
Black

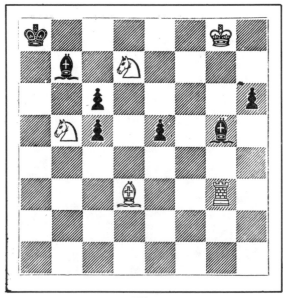

White
White to play and mate in four moves.

PUZZLE No. 141
Black

White
White to play and mate in four moves.

PUZZLE No. 142
Black

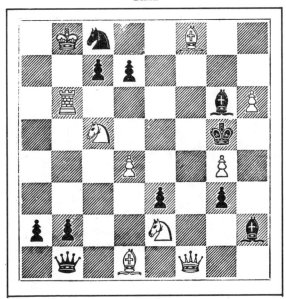

White
White to play and mate in three moves.

81

White
White to play and mate in three moves.

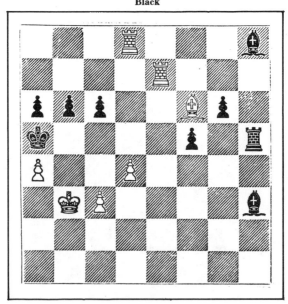

White
White to play and mate in five moves.

PUZZLE No. 145
Black

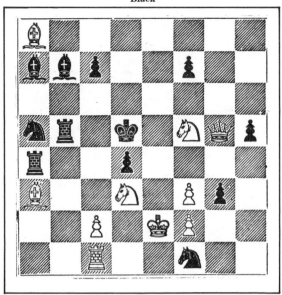

White
White to play and mate in four moves.

PUZZLE No. 146
Black

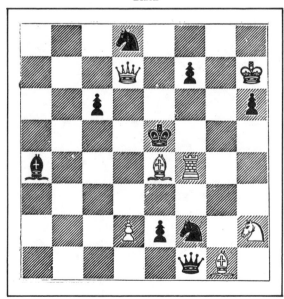

White
White to play and mate in four moves.

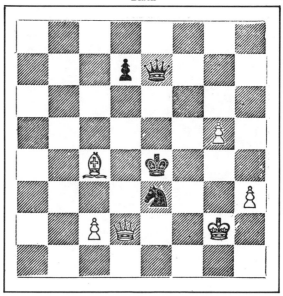

White
White to play and mate in five moves.

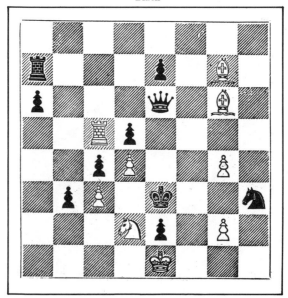

White
White to play and mate in six moves.

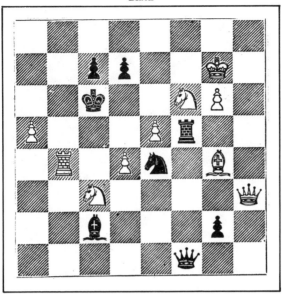

White
White to play and mate in four moves.

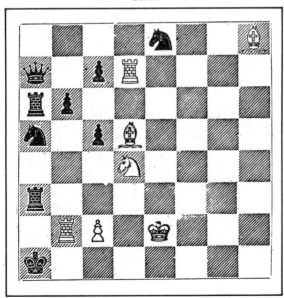

White
White to play and mate in four moves.

PUZZLE No. 151
Black

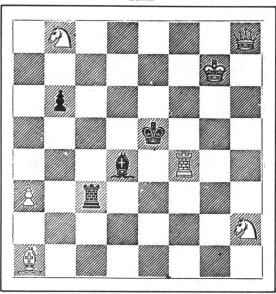

White
White to play and mate in four moves.

PUZZLE No. 152
Black

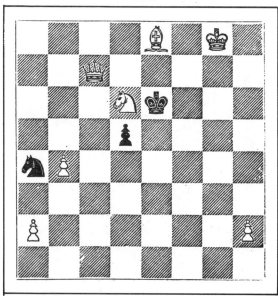

White
White to play and mate in four moves.

PUZZLE No. 153
Black

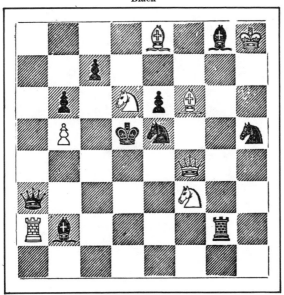

White
White to play and mate in four moves.

PUZZLE No. 154
Black

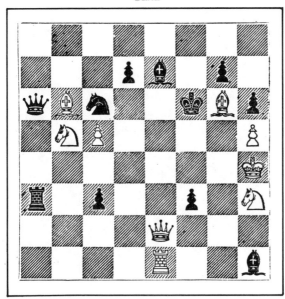

White
White to play and mate in five moves.

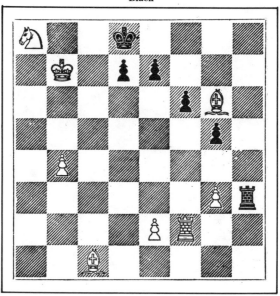

White
White to play and mate in five moves.

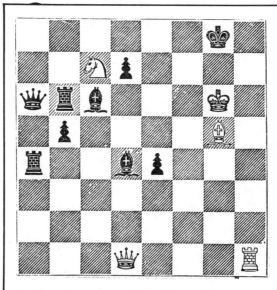

White
White to play and mate in five moves.

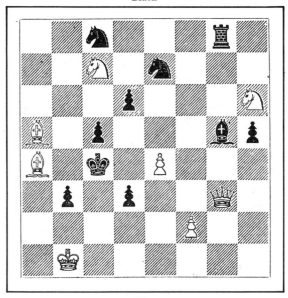

White
White to play and mate in five moves.

PUZZLE No. 158
Black

White
White to play and mate in three moves.

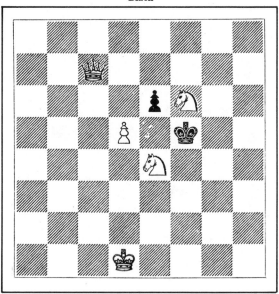

White
White to play and mate in three moves.

PUZZLE No. 160
Black

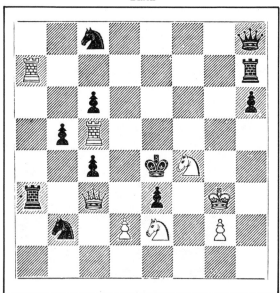

White
White to play and mate in four moves.

PUZZLE No. 161
Black

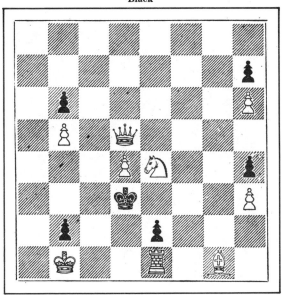

White
White to play and mate in four moves.

PUZZLE No. 162
Black

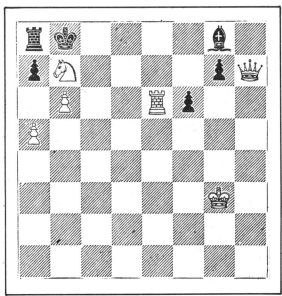

White
White to play and mate in three moves.

91

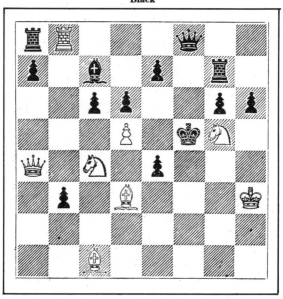

White
White to play and mate in four moves.

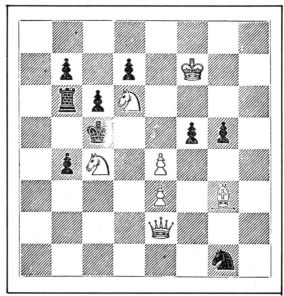

White
White to play and mate in three moves.

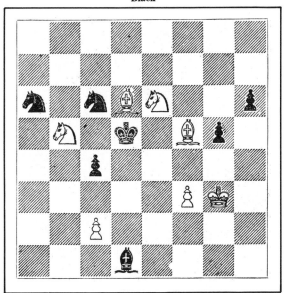

White
White to play and mate in four moves.

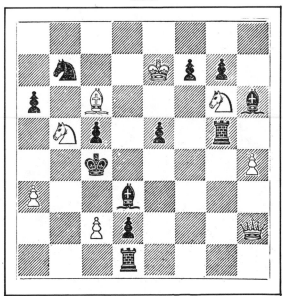

White
White to play and mate in three moves.

93

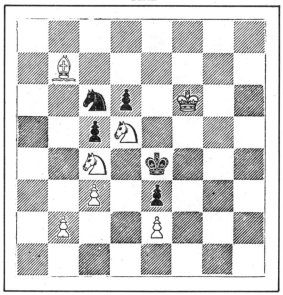

White
White to play and mate in five moves.

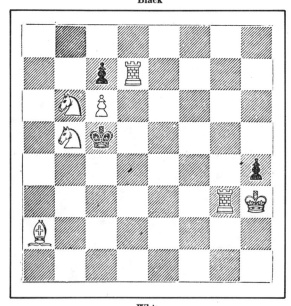

White
White to play and mate in four moves.

94

PUZZLE No. 169
Black

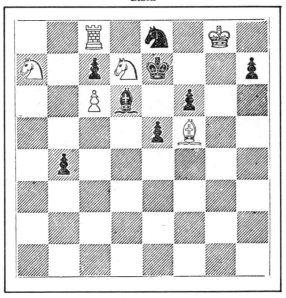

White
White to play and mate in four moves.

PUZZLE No. 170
Black

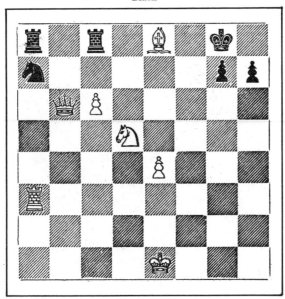

White
White to play and mate in five moves.

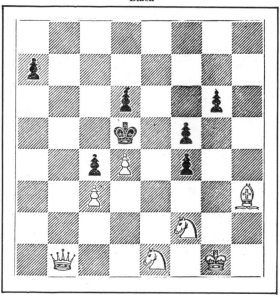

White
White to play and mate in four moves.

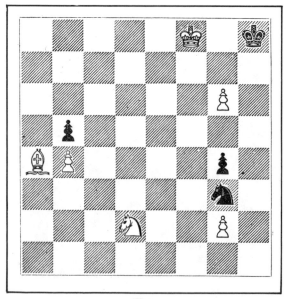

White
White to play and mate in four moves.

96

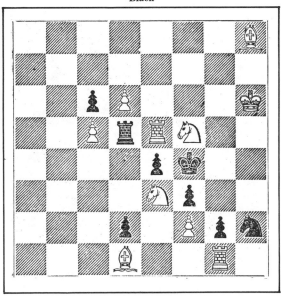

White
White to play and mate in three moves.

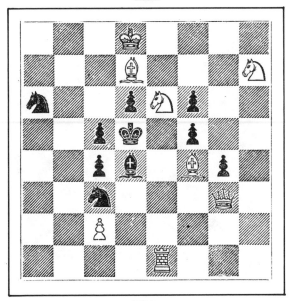

White
White to play and mate in three moves.

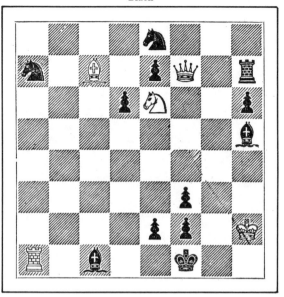

White
White to play and mate in four moves.

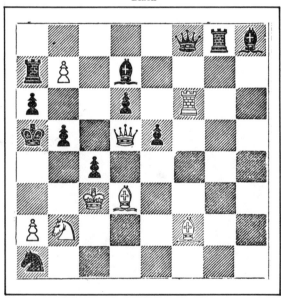

White
White to play and mate in five moves.

PUZZLE No. 177
Black

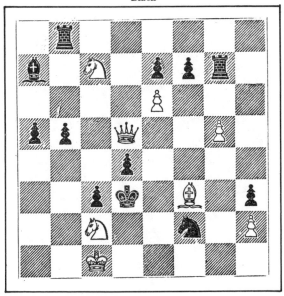

White
White to play and mate in four moves.

PUZZLE No. 178
Black

White
White to play and mate in four moves.

PUZZLE No. 179
Black

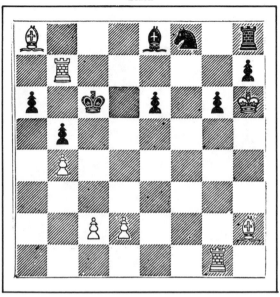

White
White to play and mate in three moves.

PUZZLE No. 180
Black

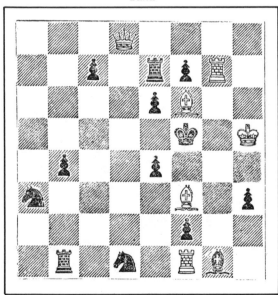

White
White to play and mate in four moves.

100

PUZZLE No. 181
Black

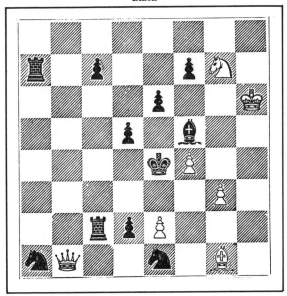

White
White to play and mate in four moves.

PUZZLE No. 182
Black

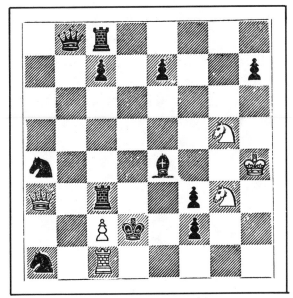

White
White to play and mate in five moves.

101

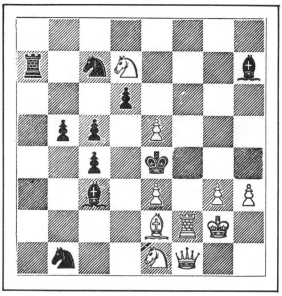

White
White to play and mate in four moves.

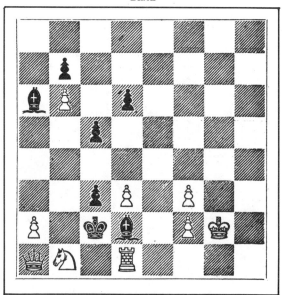

White
White to play and mate in four moves.

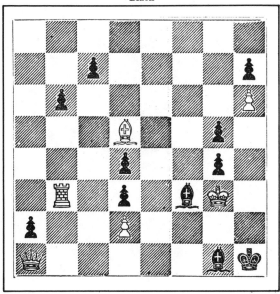

White
White to play and mate in four moves.

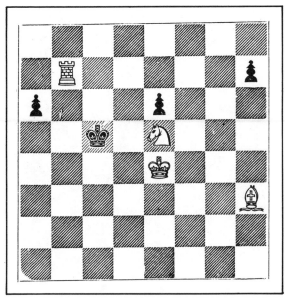

White
White to play and mate in five moves.

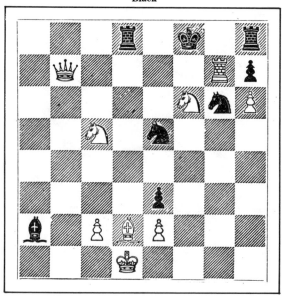

White
White to play and mate in three moves.

White
White to play and mate in five moves.

PUZZLE No. 189
Black

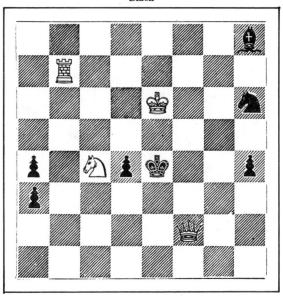

White
White to play and mate in three moves.

PUZZLE No. 190
Black

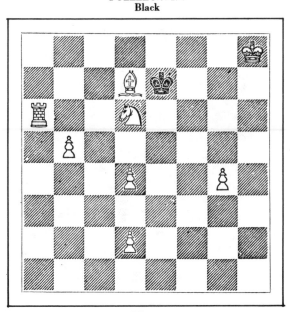

White
White to play and mate in four moves.

PUZZLE No. 191
Black

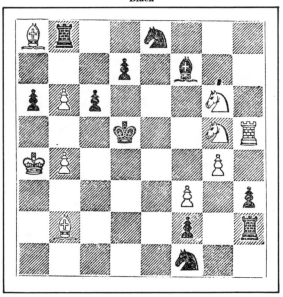

White
White to play and mate in four moves.

PUZZLE No. 192
Black

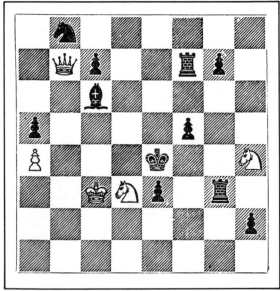

White
White to play and mate in five moves.

White
White to play and mate in three moves.

White
White to play and mate in three moves.

107

PUZZLE No. 195
Black

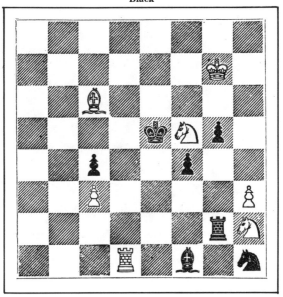

White
White to play and mate in three moves.

PUZZLE No. 196
Black

White
White to play and mate in four moves.

108

White
White to play and mate in three moves.

White
White to play and mate in three moves.

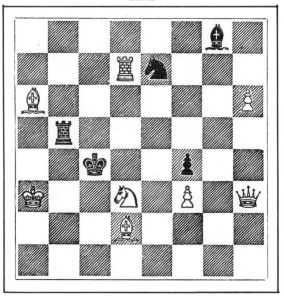

White
White to play and mate in three moves.

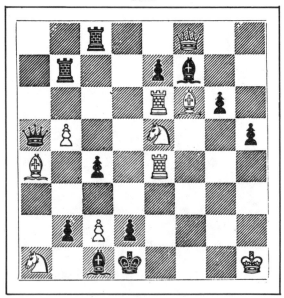

White
White to play and mate in four moves.

SOLUTIONS

PUZZLE No. 1

White	Black
1. Q x Kt	P x Q
2. B—KR7	Any move
3. Mates accordingly	

•

PUZZLE No. 2

White	Black
1. B—KB4	P x B*
2. K—Q4	B x R (best)
3. Q—QB4	Any move
4. Q or Kt mates	

*1.	Kt—Q7 (ch)
2. Q x Kt	B—Q4 (ch)
3. B x B	P x QB
4. Kt—KB7. Mate	

•

PUZZLE No. 3

White	Black
1. R—KKt5 (ch)	K x R*
2. Q—KR5 (ch)	Any move
3. B—Q. Mate	

*1.	K—K6**
2. B—KKt4 (db ch)	Any move
3. Q or R mates	

**If Black plays K elsewhere, the mate is sufficiently obvious.

•

PUZZLE No. 4

White	Black
1. Q—KB2	B—KB4*
2. R—Q7	B x R**
3. Kt—QB3	Any move
4. Q or P mates	

*1.	R from R2—R3
2. Kt—Q6	R x Kt
3. Q—K3 (ch)	K moves
4. Q mates	

**If R—Q4, then follows 3. R x R (ch) and mate next move.

•

PUZZLE No. 5

White	Black
1. Q—QR1	K—Q3*
2. Q—KR8	K x P
3. Q—Q4 (ch)	K x either Kt
4. The other Kt mates	

*1.	B—K4
2. Q x B	Any move
3. Q mates in two moves	

•

PUZZLE No. 6

White	Black
1. Q—KKt4	B x QP*
2. Q—K6	Any move
3. Q or Kt mates	

*1.	P x Kt, or K moves
2. Q x P and mate next move	

•

PUZZLE No. 7

White	Black
1. B—QB7	P—KB6
2. B—QKt8	P x P
3. P—KB4	P—Kt8, becoming a Queen or any other piece
4. B x QRP	Any move
5. B x P. Mate	

•

PUZZLE No. 8

White	Black
1. R—Q7	B x R (best)
2. Q—KKtl (ch)	K x P
3. Q—KR2	K—Q5
4. Q x B	Any move
5. Mates accordingly	

•

PUZZLE No. 9

White	Black
1. Q—QKt1	B—QKt6 (best)
2. Q—K4	B—QB5*
3. Q—Q4 (ch) and	
B or Kt mates next	
move	

*2.	P x Kt at B4**
3. Kt x B (ch)	K moves
4. B mates	

**If Black plays 2. K—Q3, then
White answers with 3. B—Kt4 (ch),
and 4. Q x Kt. Mate.

•

PUZZLE No. 10

White	Black
1. K—K8	K—Q4*
2. Q—KB8	Any move
3. Q mates	

*1.	K—KB4
2. Q—KR5 (ch)	Any move
3. Q mates	

•

PUZZLE No. 11

White	Black
1. Q—KKt7	R x Kt on QBl
2. Kt—Q7	B x Kt
3. B—KR4	Kt x B
4. Q—KB7 (ch)	K—K4 or KKt4
5. P—KB4. Mate	

PUZZLE No. 12

White	Black
i. B—K3	R x Kt*
2. Kt—QKt5	R x Kt**
3. R from KR6—K6	Any move
4. R from K4—K5.	
Mate	

*1.	P queens or P—Q7, or any other move
2. R—Q4 (ch)	K—K4
3. Kt—KB7 (ch)	K—B4
4. R—KB4. Mate	

**If Black plays K x R, then follows 3.
R—K6 (ch), and 4. Kt mates.

•

PUZZLE No. 13

White	Black
1. Kt—QB3	P x Kt (best)
2. P—QKt4	P x R
3. Kt—Q1	Any move
4. Kt mates	

•

PUZZLE No. 14

White	Black
1. Q—KR1	P—Q6*
2. P—KB4	K x Kt
3. P—KKt4 (dis ch)	

*1.	P x QBP
2. Q—QRl	P x P, or P—QB7
3. Q—KB6. Mate	

•

PUZZLE No. 15

White	Black
1. Q—KR7	R x Kt*
2. Kt—K6 (ch)	R x Kt
3. Q—QR7 (ch)	K moves
4. Q mate	

*1.   P—K5**
2. Kt—KB5 (ch)   K—K4 (best)
3. Q x R   Any move
4. Mate

**There are many other variations,
but the result in all will be found
the same.

•

PUZZLE No. 16

White	Black
1. B—KB1	B x Kt
2. Q—Q2	P x Q
3. P—K4 (dis ch)	
and mate	

•

PUZZLE No. 17

White	Black
1. B—Q4	QR—K8 (best)
2. B—K3	R x B
3. Kt—QB4	P x Kt
4. B—QR4	Any move
5. B mates	

•

PUZZLE NO. 18

White	Black
1. B—KB7	K moves
2. R—Q5	Kt x R*
3. B mates	

*If otherwise, R gives mate.

•

PUZZLE No. 19

White	Black
1. B x QRP	P—QB3*
2. Q—QKt7	Any move
3. Q gives mate	

*1.   P—K5
2. Q x P (ch)   K moves
3. B x P. Mate

•

PUZZLE No. 20

White	Black
1. Q x Kt	P x Q*
2. R—QR5	K moves where it can
3. B mates at Q2 or	
Q8, or KB4 or	
KB6, according to	
Black's last move	

*If Black plays 1. K—Q3, then follows
2. Q—Q4, etc. If Black plays 1. K—
QKt3, then we have 2. Q—QB3, etc.

•

PUZZLE No. 21

White	Black
1. Q—KR4	K x B*
2. Q—KB4	B x P
3. Q—KKt4	K—Q3 or Q5
4. Q—Q1 or Q7. Mate	

*1	B—QB7
2. Q—K1	B—QB, or B x P
3. Q—K3 (ch)	K—B7
4. Kt—QR3. Mate	

•

PUZZLE No. 22

White	Black
1. R—QR1	K x R*
2. R—KB1	P—QB6
3. P mates	

*1.	K—B6
2. Kt—Q4 (ch)	K moves
3. R mates	

•

PUZZLE No. 23

White	Black
1. Q—KKt8	P x Kt
2. R—QB2	Any move
3. Q mates	

PUZZLE No. 24

White	Black
1. Q—Q4	B x Q*
2. B—KKt6 (ch)	K—K4
3. Kt—QKt8	Any move
4. One of the Kts gives mate according to Black's play	

*1.	Q x Q**
2. B—KKt6 (ch)	K—K4
3. Kt—KB3. Mate	

**If Black plays 1. P—K4, then follows 2. Q x Kt (ch), etc. If Black plays 1. Q—KB6 (ch), we have 2. Kt x Q, and if then 2. P—K4, White replies with 3. Kt—QB7, mating next move.

PUZZLE No. 25

White	Black
1. Kt—Q4	P—Q4*
2. Q—QR6	K x Kt
3. B x R. Mate	

*If Black plays 1. K—KB5, then follows 2. Q—Q5, and mates on the next move. If Black plays 1. K x Kt, then White answers with 2. B x P (ch) and mates next move. Finally, if Black plays 1. P—KKt4, or moves its QR pawn, the reply is 2. K—K3, and mates on the following move.

PUZZLE No. 26

White	Black
1. R—Q8	K—Q3*
2. P x QP	P—QR6**
3. B—K6	Kt x B
4. Q—Q5 (ch)	Any move
5. Q or R mates	

*If Black plays 1. QP x P, then follows 2. Q—KR8 (ch), 3. Q—KB8 (ch), 4. R x P, etc. If Black makes any other first move, he accelerates his defeat.

**Black has here a choice of moves. If Black plays 2. K—K2, White replies with 3. Q—KR8, 4. Q—KB8 (ch), etc. If Black plays 2. P—KB6, then ensues 3. Q—KR2 (ch), etc. If Black plays 2. Kt—Q4, then we have 3. Q—QB6 (ch), etc. Finally, if 2. Kt—K3, the answer is 3. Q—Q5 (ch), etc.

PUZZLE No. 27

White	Black
1. Kt—KKt5 (dis ch)	Kt x R
2. Kt—KB3 (ch)	K—K5
3. K—Kt4	Any move
4. B mates at KB4 or QB5, or R mates at Q4	

PUZZLE No. 28

White	Black
1. Q x QKtP	P—Kt7 (ch)
2. Q x P	Q x B (best)
3. Q—KKt7 (ch)	Q—KB3
4. Q—QR7	Any move
5. Q—QR1. Mate	

PUZZLE No. 29

White	Black
1. Kt—QKt2 (ch)	K—QR6
2. Q—KB8*	R—KR3**
3. R—QR7 (ch)	R—QR3
4. Q x Q. Mate	

*Note that if White takes the Bishop with Queen—a step which looks almost certain to lead to victory—he will be foiled by the ingenious reply of 2. Q—QKt5.

**2.	Q x R***
3. Q x Q (ch)	R interposes
4. Q x R. Mate	

***If Black plays 2. P—KR6, then follows 3. R—QR7 (ch), and mate next move.

•

PUZZLE No. 30

White	Black
1. Q x QRP (ch)	P—QKt3 (best)*
2. Q—KKt7	B x Q (best)
3. K—Kt4	Any move
4. B or Kt mates, according to Black's play	

*If K x R, then follows 2. B—B3 (ch), 3. Q—B5 (ch), and mate next move. Again, if Black takes Queen, we have 2. K—Kt4, and 3. B or Kt mates.

•

PUZZLE No. 31

White	Black
1. Q—QR1	Kt—K3*
2. Q—KB6	Any move
3. Q mates	

*1.	B x B**
2. Q—KR8 (ch)	K moves
3. Kt mates	

**If K—B1, the answer is 2. Q—KR8 (ch) and mate next move.

•

PUZZLE No. 32

White	Black
1. Q—QKt5	Any move
2. Mates according to Black's play	

•

PUZZLE No. 33

White	Black
1. B—K4	B x B*
2. R—K5 (ch)	B x R
3. Kt mates	

*1.	P x Kt
2. R—Q5 (ch)	K moves
3. B mates	

•

PUZZLE No. 34

White	Black
1. P—QKt5	B—K4*
2. B—KR7	Any move
3. Q mates	

*1.	P—K4
2. R x Kt (ch)	K or P x R
3. Q mates	

•

PUZZLE No. 35

White	Black
1. R—QB7	R—KR3 (best)
2. Q x Q	Any move
3. Kt or Q mates	

Note: Mate can also be effected in the same number of moves by 1. R—QKt6, etc.

PUZZLE No. 36

White	Black
1. Kt—KR2	QB x RP* **
2. Kt—KKt4 (ch)	B x Kt
3. Q—KR8 (ch)	Q x Q
4. Kt x R. Mate	

*1.	B x KtP
2. Kt—KKt4 (ch)	K x R
3. Kt—QKt5 (ch)	K—QB5
4. B—Q3. Mate	

**If Black plays 1. K x R, then follows 2. Kt—QKt5 (ch), 3. Kt—KKt4 (ch), and mate next move.

•

PUZZLE No. 37

White	Black
1. B—KR5	K x R*
2. R x P (ch)	K moves
3. B mates	

*If Black plays one of his Pawns, then follows 2. R from QR8 x P, and B mates.

Note that mate can also be effected in this manner: 1. B—QB3, 2. R—QB7, mate.

•

PUZZLE No. 38

White	Black
1. P—Q4	P x Q
2. B—KB7	Kt moves
3. Kt—KB5(ch)	K moves
4. P—K7, dis mate	

•

PUZZLE No. 39

White	Black
1. R—QB1	B x Kt*
2. R—QB4 (ch)	B x B**
3. Q—K3	K—Q4
4. Kt mates	

*If Black plays Q—K8, then follows 2. Kt x Q, and mates next move. If Black plays K—K5, then 2. R—QB4 (ch), and mates next move. If Q x QBP, then 2. Kt x Q, and mates next move. Finally, if Black plays Q x QRP, then 2. Q—B3 (ch), 3. R checks, and 4. Kt mates.

**If K—Q4, then 3. R—KB4 (ch).

Note: This 1866 composition, the figures of which it will be seen represent the letter "M," was dedicated by the author, Mr. Schoumoff, to Count M. N. Mouraview, a 19th-century Russian nobleman and one of the finest chess-players in Russia.

•

PUZZLE No. 40

White	Black
1. Kt from Q1—K3	P x Kt*
2. Q—K4 (ch)	P x Q
3. R x R	Any move
4. P or R mates	

*1.	B—KR4**
2. R x P (ch)	K x R
3. Q x QP (ch)	Q x Q
4. R—K7. Mate	

**If Black plays 1. Q—QB8, then follows 2. Q—K4 (ch), 3. R x R (ch), and mate next move.

•

PUZZLE No. 41

White	Black
1. R—K1	P queens*
2. Kt—Q6 (ch)	P x Kt
3. B x P (ch)	K x B
4. Kt—Q4. Mate	

*Black has other moves, but cannot prevent the mate in four moves.

PUZZLE No. 42

White	Black
1. Kt—K1	R—QRl (ch)*
2. Q x R (ch)	K—KB5 or to Q5
3. Q—K4 (ch)	Any move
4. Q or R mates	

*1.	K—Q5**
2. Q x R	Either KP moves
3. Q—Q6 or to QKt6, according to Black's play	Any move
4. Q or R mates	

**If P—K7, then follows 2. Q—QB4 (ch), 3. Kt—Q5 (ch), and mate next move.

•

PUZZLE No. 43

White	Black
1. P—K4	B—QR4
2. Kt—KB7 (ch)	K x P (best)
3. Q—KB8	Any move
4. Q or Kt mates	

•

PUZZLE No. 44

White	Black
1. Kt—KB3	P x B*
2. Q—Q6 (ch)	K—B6
3. Q—KR2	Any move
4. Q mates	

*If P—K7, then follows 2. Q—Q2 (ch), 3. K—Kt4, and mate next move. Again, if Black plays 1. P—Q5, then we have 2. B—KKt6, 3. Q—Q3, and mate next move.

•

PUZZLE No. 45

White	Black
1. Kt—K5	K x Kt*
2. Q—KKt4	K x R**
3. Q—Q4. Mate	

*1.	P x B***
2. Q—KKt4 (ch)	K moves
3. Q or R mates	

**If K—KB3, or B x R, the White Bishop x P, giving mate.

***If B x R, then follows 2. Q—KB3 (ch), and 3. B mates. If K—B5, then comes 2. Q—KKt4 (ch), and mate next move.

•

PUZZLE No. 46

White	Black
1. Kt—KB7	K—KB4*
2. Q—K6 (ch)	K moves
3. Q mates	

*1.	K—KKt6
2. Q—KKt1 (ch)	K moves
3. Q mates	

Note: The chessmen in this puzzle are arranged to represent a capital letter "S," since the puzzle, created by Mr. Schoumoff of St. Petersburg in 1866, was dedicated to H. Staunton.

•

PUZZLE No. 47

White	Black
1. K—KKt8	P—Q4*
2. Kt—QR7	Any move
3. Kt mates	

*Black has a bountiful choice of moves here at command, but, play what he will, the result is the same.

•

PUZZLE No. 48

White	Black
1. R x KP	P—QB4*
2. R—QB4 (best)	Any move
3. Mates	

*1.   P x R (dis ch)
2. B x R   Any move
3. Mates

•

PUZZLE No. 49

White	Black
1. Kt from Q5—K3	K x R*
2. Q—QKt4 (ch)	K or R x Q
3. Kt mates	

*If Black plays R x B, the reply is 2.
Q—QB3 and 3. Q mates. If Black
plays 1. R—K5, or 1. K—K3, or
1. K x P, then follows 2. Kt x P and
mate next move. Finally, if 1. Q x B,
White answers with 2. Kt—QB4 (ch)
and 3. Q—K5, mate.

•

PUZZLE No. 50

White	Black
1. Q x QP	Kt—Q6 (best)
2. Q x Kt	P x Q
3. B mates	

•

PUZZLE No. 51

White	Black
1. R—K4	R—QR8 (best)
2. Kt—QKt5	K x R (best)
3. R—K6 (ch)	K moves
4. Kt mates	

•

PUZZLE No. 52

White	Black
1. Kt—QR2 (dis ch)	R—Q5
2. Kt—QKt4	P moves
3. R—QR4	P moves
4. K—Q3. Mate	

•

PUZZLE No. 53

White	Black
1. B—Q3	P—QB7
2. B x QKtP	K x B
3. B—QR4, and	
R mates next move	

•

PUZZLE No. 54

White	Black
1. Q—QB5	Q x Q*
2. Kt—K4 (ch)	R x Kt
3. Kt—KKt5	Any move
4. Kt mates	

*1	P—KKt4**
2. Kt x Kt (ch)	K—Kt3
3. Kt—K7 (ch)	K moves
4. P x P. Mate	

**Black has a great choice of moves,
but in no case can he prolong
the game beyond the stipulated point.
If Black plays 1. Kt—KB5, then
follows 2. Kt x Kt, 3. Q—Q4, and Kt
mates; or 3. Kt—Q5 (ch), and Kt x Q,
mate, according to Black's second
move. If Black plays 1. Q x P, we
have 2. Kt x Kt (ch), 3. Q x Q, and 4.
Q mates. If, again, Black plays 1.
Kt—K2, White answers with 2. Kt—
KKt5, etc.

Note: If White attempts to mate by 1.
Kt—K4 (ch), 2. Kt—KKt5, he will
be foiled by Black playing 2. Kt—
QB4.

•

PUZZLE No. 55

White	Black
1. Q—Q2	K—QB5 or K5
2. B—K6 or	
QB6 (ch)	P—Q4
3. K—QB2 or K2	B—QB6 or K6*
4. Q x B. Mate	

*3.	B moves
4. B x P. Mate	

120

PUZZLE No. 56

White	Black
1. R x KP	P x R (best)*
2. Kt—Q4	BP x Kt
3. R—K5	P x R
4. Kt—B5	P x Kt
5. Q—R6. Mate	

*1.	B x R
2. P—Kt5 (ch)	K—K3
3. Q—R3 (ch)	B—B4
4. Q x B. Mate	

•

PUZZLE No. 57

White	Black
1. P—K3	Kt—KB5 or K2*
2. P—K4. Mate	

*If Black plays 1. Kt x P, then we have 2. Q—KB2, mate. If 1. Q x P, or Q—QKt3, then follows 2. Q x Kt, mate. And, if 1. K—K4, then 2. Kt—Q4, dis ch and mate.

•

PUZZLE No. 58

White	Black
1. R x KP	Any move
2. R or B mates	

•

PUZZLE No. 59

White	Black
1. Q—QR2	K x R*
2. Kt—Q6 (ch)	K moves
3. Q mates	

*1.	K—Q6**
2. R—KB3 (ch)	K—K5
3. Kt mates	

**If Black moves K—Q4, the reply is 2. R x P (ch), and Q mates next move.

PUZZLE No. 60

White	Black
1. Q—QR4	B x Q*
2. R—QB3	Any move
3. Kt mates	

*1.	Kt x Q**
2. Kt—Q3 (ch)	Q x Kt
3. P—KB4. Mate	

**Black has many other moves, but none by which he can postpone the mate.

•

PUZZLE No. 61

White	Black
1. R—KKt1	K or B moves
2. Kt—KKt6	KB or P moves
3. Kt mates	

•

PUZZLE No. 62

White	Black
1. R—K8	R x R
2. B—QB6	B—K7
3. Q—KB2 (ch)	Kt x Q
4. B—KKt5. Mate	

•

PUZZLE No. 63

White	Black
1. B—KR7	P—KKt4*
2. R—Q6 (dis ch)	R—K4
3. Kt mates	

*Black has a variety of defenses, but the result is the same in every case. If Black plays 1. P—KR5, the reply is 2. R x KKtP, etc. If 1. P—QB5, then 2. R x BP (dis ch), etc. If 1. B—Q2, the answer is 2. R—KB7 (dis ch), etc. And, finally, if Black plays 1. P—K7, White moves 2. R—KB3 (dis ch), etc.

PUZZLE No. 64

White	Black
1. Q—KR8	K—KKt5*
2. Q—KR5 (ch)	K x Q
3. Kt—KB6, mate	

*1.	R x Kt**
2. Q—KR5 (ch)	K moves
3. Q or B mates	

**1.	B—KR5
2. Q—KR5 (ch)	Any move
3. Q mates	

●

PUZZLE No. 65

White	Black
1. Q x P	P x Q*
2. B—Q4 (ch)	K x Kt
3. B—K4 (the meeting of the Bishops). Mate	

*Black has a choice of moves. Black may play 1. B—QB4, or 1. Kt—QB3, or 1. B—QR6, or 1. K x Kt— but in no case can Black protract his defeat beyond the stipulated point.

●

PUZZLE No. 66

White	Black
1. Q—QKt1	P x Kt*
2. Q x P (ch)	K moves
3. B or Q mates	

*1.	B—K2 (ch)**
2. K—QR4	Any move
3. Q or R mates	

**If 1. P—KKt3, then follows 2. R x B, and 3. R, or Q, or Kt gives mate.

●

PUZZLE No. 67

White	Black
1. B—Q5	K—Q3*
2. B—QR8	K—QB2
3. Kt—Q5. Mate	

*1.	K—Q5
2. Q—KB3	P moves
3. Kt—QB6. Mate	

●

PUZZLE No. 68

White	Black
1. Kt—Q2	P x Kt*
2. Kt—KB1	P—K4**
3. Kt—K3 (ch)	K—K3
4. P—Q5. Mate	

*If Black plays R—QB2, then follows 2. Kt x R, 3. Kt—K8, etc. If R—Q2, or R—QKt2, the answer is 2. R x R, etc. Finally, if P—K4, White plays R x R and mates with Kt next move.

**Black has other moves, but the result will easily be seen to be the same.

●

PUZZLE No. 69

White	Black
1. P—QKt4	Kt—QR5 (best)
2. B—K2	R—QB6 (best)
3. R—Q7 (ch)	K moves
4. Kt—K5. Mate	

●

PUZZLE No. 70

White	Black
1. B—QKt6	Kt—K4 or KR7 (ch)*
2. Q x Kt (ch)	Any move
3. Q or R mates	

*1.	P—KB4 (ch)
2. K—B4	Any move
3. Q or R mates	

PUZZLE No. 71

White	Black
1. Kt—KB4	P—KR5 (best)
2. Q—QR7	Any move
3. Q mates	

●

PUZZLE No. 72

White	Black
1. Q—KKt6	P x Q*
2. K—QB2	P x B, or P or Kt moves
3. Mates accordingly	

*1.	Kt—K3
2. R—QB3	K x Kt
3. Q mates	

●

PUZZLE No. 73

White	Black
1. Kt—QR8	P—Kt5
2. B—KKt7	Any move
3. B mates	

●

PUZZLE No. 74

White	Black
1. R—QKt6	P x R, or B—QR4*
2. Kt—QI	Any move
3. Kt mates	

*1.	B—KB4
2. B x KP	Any move
3. B mates	

Note: If White attempts to mate by 1. R—Q3, he can be foiled by B—KB4. If he tries to mate by 1. R—KB6, he can be defeated by B—QR4 and then B—QB2.

●

PUZZLE No. 75

White	Black
1. R from QKt5—KR5	P x R*
2. R—QR2	P—QKt3 or 4
3. B x Kt (ch)	R interposes
4. Kt mates	

*1.	B—QB4**
2. R—QR2 (ch)	Kt—QR2
3. P x B	Any move
4. Kt mates	

**Black may also play R—KRI. In that case the answer is 2. R x R (ch), 3. R—QR2, and mate next move.

●

PUZZLE No. 76

White	Black
1. R—QR5	Q x Q*
2. B—KR3 (ch)	K—B2**
3. Kt—K5(ch)	K—K1
4. R mates	

*If Black plays Q—KB3, the reply is 2. Kt—K5, and then mate as above. If Black plays K—B2, the answer is 2. Kt checks, etc.

**If Black plays K—Q4, then follows 3. R checks and B mates.

Note: The solution given is fine, but there is an even easier one, beginning 1. Q x Q (ch), 2. Kt—QB (ch), 3. R—QB3, etc.

●

PUZZLE No. 77

White	Black
1. B—KB1	K—B6*
2. Q—QB4 (ch)	K—Q7
3. Q—QBI. Mate	

*If Black moves K—K6, then White plays 2. Q—Kt (ch), etc. If Black

123

moves K—B4, the reply must be 2. Q
x RP (ch), etc. Lastly, if Black moves
either P, the answer is 2. Q—B4 (ch),
and mate next move.

●

PUZZLE No. 78

WHITE	BLACK
1. Kt—QKt4	K—KB4*
2. Q—KKt2	K moves
3. Q—Q5. Mate	

*1	K—Q5 or 3**
2. Q—QB6	Any move
3. Q mates	

**If to K3, White obviously mates at
once.

●

PUZZLE No. 79

WHITE	BLACK
1. B—K4	B—Q4, or Kt x R or P, or P—QB6 (ch), or P—QKt6, or any other move
2. Kt—K2, mate; or R x B, mate; or B—K2, mate; or P x P, mate; or Q mates; or R—Q5, mate	

●

PUZZLE No. 80

WHITE	BLACK
1. R—K5	R—K8*
2. B—K4	Any move
3. R or new Q mates	

*If B—QB3, White takes B and gives
mate with R or new Q.

●

PUZZLE No. 81

WHITE	BLACK
1. B—KB5	Kt—QB3 (ch)*
2. K—QKt6	Any move
3. Q mates	

*1.	Kt—QB5 (ch)**
2. K x P (ch)	Any move
3. Q mates	

**If Kt—Q7, White replies with 2.
Q—QB6 (ch), and mates with B next
move. If Kt—Q6, White answers with
2. Q—QB4 (ch), and mates next move.

●

PUZZLE No. 82

WHITE	BLACK
1. R—KB2	P x R*
2. B—KB1	Any move
3. R—QB4. Mate	

*If Kt x B, or Kt—QKt4, then comes
2. R—QB2 (ch) and mate next move.

●

PUZZLE No. 83

WHITE	BLACK
1. Kt—KR1	R—QKt6*
2. Q—KB1	R x Q**
3. Kt—KB2	Any move
4. R or Kt mates	

*1.	R—KB4***
2. R—QB7 (ch)	K x P
3. R—QKt7 and then mates with R next move	

**If any other move, White responds
with 3. Q x B or R.

***1.	Q—K2
2. P x Q	K x P
3. P—K6 (ch)	Any move
4. Q or R mates	

124

PUZZLE No. 84

WHITE	BLACK
1. Kt—K2	P—QB5*
2. Q—K2 (ch)	K moves
3. Q or Kt mates	

*1.	P—K5
2. Q—QR2 (ch)	K moves
3. Q mates	

•

PUZZLE No. 85

WHITE	BLACK
1. R—KKt6	K—K5*
2. B—KKt3	K—Q4
3. B—KB3 (ch)	K moves
4. R—QB6. Mate	

*1.	K—K4
2. B—KKt3 (ch)	K—K5**
3. R—QB6	K moves
4. B mates	

**If K—Q4, White B checks and mates with R as above.

•

PUZZLE No. 86

WHITE	BLACK
1. R—K4	P—Q3 or P—QKt4
2. KB—KR3	P moves
3. QB—KB4	P x B
4. KB x P. Mate	

•

PUZZLE No. 87

WHITE	BLACK
1. Kt—KR3	P x Kt*
2. B—KKt7	P—R7
3. K—QB4	P queens
4. R—K5. Mate	

*1.	K—Q5
2. B—KKt7 (ch)	K—K5

3. K—QB4	P x Kt
4. R—K5. Mate	

•

PUZZLE No. 88

WHITE	BLACK
1. Kt—K4 (ch)	Kt x Kt
2. R x P at Q3 (ch)	P x R
3. B—QKt4	R x B (or mate next move)
4. R—Q5 (ch)	K—K2
5. R x B (ch)	K moves
6. R—Q8 (ch), and draws by perpetual check; or, if Black plays K—KR3, White checks at KR7 with R, obliging K to take R, and is stalemated.	

•

PUZZLE No. 89

WHITE	BLACK
1. B—Q8	B x P (best)
2. B—QKt6 (ch)	K—K5
3. Kt—QB5 (ch)	K—Q5
4. Kt—K6 (ch)	K—K5
5. Kt—KKt5. Mate	

•

PUZZLE No. 90

WHITE	BLACK
1. R x P (ch)	P x R (best)
2. R—QB6	Q x R*
3. Kt—Kt8	Any move
4. P or Kt mates	

*2.	B—Kt3
3. Kt—B7 (ch)	B x Kt**
4. P mates	

**If Kt x Kt, then White plays R x B and mates.

PUZZLE No. 91

White	Black
1, Kt—Q8 (ch)	K—Q4*
2. R—QKt5 (ch)	K—QB5
3. Kt—Q6 (ch)	K—Q5
4. Kt—K6. Checkmate	

*1.	K—K4
2. R—QKt5 (ch)	Q—Q4
3. P—Q4. Mate	

•

PUZZLE No. 92

White	Black
1. R—QKt6	Q x B (best)
2. Kt—Q7 (ch)	P x R (best)
3. Q—KB7 (ch)	R x Q
4. R—Q6. Mate	

•

PUZZLE No. 93

White	Black
1. Q—K1 (ch)	K—Q1
2. R—KB8 (ch)	K x R
3. Q—QR5 (ch)	K—Q3
4. Q—K5 (ch)	K x Q
5. B—KB4. Mate	

•

PUZZLE No. 94

White	Black
1. R—QB4 (ch)	Kt x R
2. Kt—Q5	K or B x Kt
3. B mates	

•

PUZZLE No. 95

White	Black
1. B x P	K—KB4*
2. Kt—Q5 (dis ch)	K—KKt5**
3. R—KB4 (ch)	K—KR6 or KKt6
4. B—KB2	K moves
5. Kt—K3	K moves
6. R mates	

*1.	K—KB3
2. Kt—Q5 (ch)	K—K3***
3. Kt—QB3	K moves
4. P—Q4 (ch)	K moves
5. B—QKt6	K moves
6. R—KB6. Mate	

**If 2. K—KKt3 or 4, White plays 3. R—KKt2 (ch), and mates within the stipulated number of moves; and if 2. K—K4, White plays 3. K—Q7 and mates next move.

***If K—K4, White mates in four moves.

Note: The variations in this ingenious puzzle are too numerous to list, but those given will suffice to enable any player to discover the remainder.

•

PUZZLE No. 96

White	Black
1. K moves	K—Q3
2. Kt—QKt5 (ch)	K moves
3. R—QB7	K x the other Rook
4. Kt mates	

•

PUZZLE No. 97

White	Black
1. Q—KB3	P—K5 (best)
2. Q—Q1 and mate next move	

•

PUZZLE No. 98

White	Black
1. Q—K8 (ch)	K—QB3
2. R—KKt2	K moves
3. Q—K1 (ch)	P x Q
4. R—QR2 (ch)	K moves
5. Kt—QB7. Mate	

PUZZLE No. 99

White	Black
1. B—QKt5	B—K8*
2. Q—KKt5 (ch)	Kt x Q
3. Kt mates	

*1.	Kt x P
2. Kt—KB4 (ch)	K—K4
3. B x Kt. Mate	

•

PUZZLE No. 100

White	Black
1. QR—KB7 (dis ch)	R—K4
2. KR—KR6	P—QKt3
3. KR—KB6	R moves
4. KR moves (dis ch and mate)	

•

PUZZLE No. 101

White	Black
1. R—KKt6	R—KR5 (best)
2. Kt—QB5	R x Q (best)
3. R—KKt5	Any move
4. Mate	

•

PUZZLE No. 102

White	Black
1. B—B5	P—Q6*
2. B—R7	P—Kt3
3. K x B	K moves
4. K—B6 (dis ch and mate)	

*1.	P—KKt3
2. P—Q3	P x B
3. K—Kt6	P moves
4. P x P. Mate	

•

PUZZLE No. 103

White	Black
1. P—Kt4 (ch)	B x P (best)
2. QKt—QB3	B x B (best)
3. B—Q5	K—K4 (best)
4. Q—KB6 (ch)	K x B
5. Kt mates	

•

PUZZLE No. 104

White	Black
1. Kt—KKt3	P x P (best)
2. R x P	Kt x R*
3. P—K3 and mate next move	

*If Black plays 2. B—KB4, then follows 3. R—QB5 (ch) and mate next move.

•

PUZZLE No. 105

White	Black
1. R—QKt8	Either R x Q* **
2. Kt—KB5 (ch)	K—Q1
3. B—QKt7, dis ch and mate	

*1.	B—Q2
2. B x B	P x Kt***
3. R—K8. Mate	

**Black has many other modes of play, but cannot delay the mate. If 1. P x K, then follows 2. Kt—Kt8 (ch), and mate next move. If 1. P—QB3 or QB4, then follows 2. Kt—KB5 (ch), and 3. Q mates. If 1. R—QR1, White replies 2. Kt—Kt8 (ch), and 3. Kt—QKt7. Mate.

***If 2. B x Q, or 2. R—QR1, then ensues 3. Kt—B5. Mate.

•

127

PUZZLE No. 106

WHITE	BLACK
1. Kt—K7	R x Kt* **
2. K—B2	Kt—K4 (best)
3. K—K2	Q x B***
4. Kt x B (ch)	R x Kt
5. R—Q5. Mate	

*1.	B x B
2. K—B2	Kt—K4 (best)
3. K—K2	Kt x P (best)
4. Kt—B3 (ch)	K moves
5. P x Kt. Mate	

**If Black gives check with Kt, or B or Kt x Kt, White plays K—K2 and mates in two more moves. Again, if Black plays 1. B—QR4, White plays Kt x P, checking, and then mates with R.

***If B x B, or Kt x P, or B—QB4, or R—QB2, White checks with P and mates next move with B.

•

PUZZLE No. 107

WHITE	BLACK
1. R—KKt3	K moves
2. R—KKt6	Kt—Kt2*
3. R—QB7 (ch)	Any move
4. Kt mates	

*2.	B x R (or any move)
3. R x P (ch)	R x R
4. Kt mates	

•

PUZZLE No. 108

WHITE	BLACK
1. Kt—KR6	K—QB4*
2. Kt—KB7	Any move
3. Kt mates at K5 or Q6	

*If 1. B—QB5, White answers with 2. Kt—KKt4, and mates next move.

PUZZLE No. 109

WHITE	BLACK
1. Kt—QKt5 (ch)	K—K5 (best)
2. Kt—KB4	B—QB4
3. Kt—KR2 and mates next move	

•

PUZZLE No. 110

WHITE	BLACK
1. R—KB4	Kt x R*
2. Kt—KR4	Any move
3. Kt mates	

*1.	Kt at Q5 moves**
2. R—B5 (ch)	Any move
3. Q—Q5. Mate	

**If 1. Q x QBP, then follows 2. Kt—QB4 (ch), and 3. Kt—K3 (dis ch and mate). Again, if 1. Q x QP, then ensues 2. Kt—KKt4 (ch), and Kt—K3 (dis ch and mate).

•

PUZZLE No. 111

WHITE	BLACK
1. Q x QP (ch)	P x Q
2. R—QB5	Any move
3. Kt or R mates	

•

PUZZLE No. 112

WHITE	BLACK
1. R—QB5 (ch)	P x R*
2. B—QB6	P x B**
3. Kt—K3 (ch)	Q x Kt
4. Q—K8 (ch)	K—K4
5. R—KB5 (ch)	K x R
6. Q—KB6. Mate	

*1.	K x R
2. Q—QB3 (ch)	K—Q4
3. Kt—K3 (ch)	Q x Kt
4. Q—QB4 (ch)	K—K4

5. Q—K6 (ch)   K x R
6. Q—KB6. Mate

**If black plays 2. K x B, then follows
3. Q—QB8 (ch), 4. Kt—K3 (ch), etc.

•

PUZZLE No. 113

WHITE	BLACK
1. Q—KKt1	P moves*
2. Q—KKt7	Any move
3. Q mates	

*1.	K—Q4**
2. Q—KKt4, and	
mates next move	

**If 1. K—QB5, then follows 2. Q—Ql
and mate next move.

•

PUZZLE No. 114

WHITE	BLACK
1. B x KRP (ch)	K x B*
2. R—KKt5	K x R
3. P—KKt8,	
becoming	
a Q (ch)	K moves
4. QKt or P mates	

*1.	K—KR7
2. B—KB2	K—KR8
3. P—KR6, and	
mates next move	

•

PUZZLE No. 115

WHITE	BLACK
1. R—Q2	Kt—QB6*
2. K—K6 (dis ch)	K—K1
3. R—QB2 and wins	

*1.	Kt—K6
2. K—QB6	K—QB1
3. R—K2 and wins	

PUZZLE No. 116

WHITE	BLACK
1. R—Q5 (ch)	K—QB5*
2. B—QB2	P—Q3**
3. B—QR4	Kt moves***
4. R—Q4. Mate	

*If Kt is interposed, White takes it,
giving mate at once.

**If Black takes the R, then B mates
at QKt3. If Black plays away the Kt,
then R mates at QB5.

***If K x R, mate follows, as before
mentioned, by B—QKt3.

•

PUZZLE No. 117

WHITE	BLACK
1. Kt from Q7—K	R—KKt3*
2. K—B2	R—B3 (ch)
3. K—Kt3	Any move
4. Q or Kt mates	

*1.	R—KB1 (ch)
2. K—Kt2	R—B3
3. K—Kt3 and	
mate next move	

•

PUZZLE No. 118

WHITE	BLACK
1. B—QKt5	K—K3* **
2. Q—KB5 (ch)	K x Q***
3. B—Q7	

*1.	R—B8 or
	R—QR3
2. Q x P (ch)	K moves
3. Q—Q7 or	
Q—KKt7. Mate	

**If Black plays 1. K—Q3, then
follows 2. Q—KB7, etc. If 1. K—Q1,
then White moves 2. Q x P and mates
next move.

***If Black moves otherwise, the Q gives mate.

•

PUZZLE No. 119

WHITE	BLACK
1. B—Q5	K—QR5 (best)
2. B—QB6 (ch)	K—QKt6
3. P—Q3	Kt—K5 or K6
4. Kt—K6	Any move
5. Kt—QR5 or Q4 (ch)	B or Kt x Kt
6. Kt mates	

•

PUZZLE No. 120

WHITE	BLACK
1. Kt—QR7	Q—QR6*
2. Q—QKt1 (ch)	K—QB6
3. Kt mates	

*1.	P—QKt6
2. Kt—QKt5 (ch)	Q or R moves
3. Q mates	

•

PUZZLE No. 121

WHITE	BLACK
1. Q—QB1	B—K6 (ch)*
2. Q x B (ch)	Kt x Q
3. Kt—KB6. Mate	

*Black has here a variety of moves. If 1. B—QKt3, or R—QR4, then follows 2. Kt—K5 (ch), and mate next move. If 1. B—QKt4, then comes 2. Kt—Q2 (ch), and mate next move. If 1. Kt—K7, White replies with 2. Kt—KR4 (ch), and mate next move. If 1. B—QKt8, or P—QKt6, then ensues 2. Q—QB4 (ch), and mate next move. And lastly, if 1. B—QB4 or to KKt8, White's play is 2. Q x B, mating on the following move.

PUZZLE No. 122

WHITE	BLACK
1. Kt—KKt1	K moves
2. Kt—KR3	K—KB2*
3. Kt—KKt5. Mate	

*2.	K—Q4**
3. Kt—KB4. Mate	

**If 2. K—KB4, then follows 3. B—Q7. Mate.

•

PUZZLE No. 123

WHITE	BLACK
1. Q—K7 (ch)	K x Kt at Q4*
2. Kt—QR3	Any move
3. QB or Kt mates in six different ways, according to Black's play	

*1.	K x the other Kt
2. Q—QB7 (ch) and mate next move	

•

PUZZLE No. 124

WHITE	BLACK
1. Q—QKt1	P x P
2. Q—QB2	Any move
3. Q, B, or Kt mates	

•

PUZZLE No. 125

WHITE	BLACK
1. Kt—QKt4 (ch)	P x Kt
2. P—QKt3	P—K5 (best)
3. Q—QB7	Kt—QKt2 (best)
4. Q—QB4 (ch)	K moves
5. Q—K6. Mate	

Note: There is, of course, an even shorter road to victory:

1. Kt—KB2	P—QB5 (best)
2. Q—Q2 (ch), and mate next move	

PUZZLE No. 126

WHITE	BLACK
1. Kt—QR6	Q x B*
2. Q x Kt (ch)	Q—Q4**
3. Kt—KB7	Q x Q
4. Kt—QB7. Mate	

*Black may also play B—QB1, or B—K1, or P—KB4, but in every case the mate is inevitable within the stipulated number of moves.

**If K x Kt, then follows 3. Q—Q4 (ch), and mate next move.

•

PUZZLE No. 127

WHITE	BLACK
1. B—QB1 (ch)	R—K6 (best)
2. R x P	R x R (best)
3. Q—KR8	Any move
4. Kt checks	R x Kt
5. Q mates	

•

PUZZLE No. 128

WHITE	BLACK
1. Q—QB8	P—K5 (best)
2. R x P (ch)	B x R
3. Kt—QKt5 (ch)	K moves
4. P mates	

•

PUZZLE No. 129

WHITE	BLACK
1. Q—Q1	K—Q4*
2. Q—KKt4	K x P
3. Q—Q7. Mate	

*1.	K—B4
2. Q—KKt4 (ch)	K moves
3. Q—KKt6. Mate	

•

PUZZLE No. 130

WHITE	BLACK
1. Kt—KB5	P x Kt* **
2. R—K6 (ch)	K—Q4 (best)
3. R x P (ch), and mate follows in two moves	

*1.	Kt—KR5
2. Kt—K7	P—K4 (best)
3. B—Kt7, mating in the two next moves	

**If Black plays 1. K—K4, the reply is 2. B—KKt7, and mate in two more moves. If Black plays 1. K—Q4, then follows 2. Kt—K7, and mate in two moves.

•

PUZZLE No. 131

WHITE	BLACK
1. Q—QKt7	B—K3*
2. Q—KB3	B x Kt
3. Q x Kt (ch)	K x Q
4. B x P. Mate	

*1.	Kt—Q4**
2. Q—KKt7 (ch)	Kt interposes
3. Q—K7 (ch), mating next move	

**Black has other defenses, but none of them can avert the mate.

•

PUZZLE No. 132

WHITE	BLACK
1. Kt—QKt5	P x Kt
2. Q x Kt at QR1	Q—KR1*
3. B—KKt8	Any move
4. Q mates	

*2.	B x P
3. Q—QR8 (ch)	Q interposes
4. Q x Q. Mate	

PUZZLE No. 133

WHITE	BLACK
1. K—R3	
	All Black's
2. K—Kt4	moves are
3. K—B5	compulsory
4. K—K4 (dis ch and mate)	

●

PUZZLE No. 134

WHITE	BLACK
1. Kt—Q8 (ch)	K—Q4 (best)
2. Q x Q (ch)	K x Q (best)
3. B—KR4 (dis ch)	K—Q5*
4. Kt or B mates	

*3.	K—B5
4. K—K2	Any move
5. Kt—K6. Mate	

●

PUZZLE No. 135

WHITE	BLACK
1. Kt—Q2	B x P*
2. R—Q4	Any move
3. Kt mates	

*1.	B x Kt, or any move
2. R—B4 (ch)	Any move
3. Kt or P mates	

●

PUZZLE No. 136

WHITE	BLACK
1. Q—KB6	K—Q5 (best)
2. Q—KB2 (ch)	K x Kt
3. Q—KB6 (ch)	K x Q, or K moves
4. Kt or Q mates	

●

PUZZLE No. 137

WHITE	BLACK
1. Kt x KP	K—B5*
2. Q—KB1 (ch)	K—Q4
3. P—QR4	K moves
4. Q mates	

*1.	K—QB7** ***
2. Q—QR1	K—Q6
3. Q—Q1 (ch)	K moves
4. Q mates	

**If K—K7, then follows 2. Q—QB1, 3. Q—Q1 (ch), and mate next move.

***1.	K x Kt
2. Q—Q4 (ch)	K—B4
3. K—K5 or Q5 (ch)	K moves
4. Q mates	

●

PUZZLE No. 138

WHITE	BLACK
1. Kt—K5	Kt—KB1 or Kt—KKt6*
2. Q—Q3	Any move
3. Q or Kt mates	

*If B x B, then follows 2. Q—K2, and 3. Q or Kt mates.

●

PUZZLE No. 139

WHITE	BLACK
1. B—QB7 (ch)	R x B
2. Q x QP	P x Q*
3. Kt—KKt6 (ch)	K moves
4. B mates	

*Black has a variety of moves at this crisis, but none which will retard the mate.

●

132

PUZZLE No. 140

White	Black
1. B—K4	B—QB8 (best)
2. R—KKt6	B or P moves
3. R—QBP	B x R, or any move
4. B x B. Mate	

•

PUZZLE No. 141

White	Black
1. Kt—KB7 (ch)	K—Q4*
2. Kt—Q8	K—K4**
3. B—QB3	Any move
4. Kt from Q4—K6. Mate	

*1.	K—KB3
2. Q—KB5 (ch)	K—KKt2
3. Kt—K6 (ch)	K—KKt1
4. Q—KKt6. Checkmate	

**If 2. K—QB4, White plays 3. Kt—QKt3 (ch), and mate next move. If 2. Kt—Q3, Kt—K6, or any Pawn is moved, then follows 3. Kt—K6 (dis ch) and mate next move. If 2. Kt—Q7, White answers with 3. Kt—QB6 (ch), etc.

•

PUZZLE No. 142

White	Black
1. Kt—KKt1	P x R* **
2. Q—KB4 (ch)	K x Q, or K—KR5
3. Kt or Q mates	

*1.	Q—KB4
2. Kt—K4 (ch)	Q x Kt or K—KR5
3. Q—KB6 or Q—KR3. Mate	

**If 1. Q x B, White answers 2. R x B (ch), and 3. Q mates. If 1. P—K7, then follows 2. Q—KB6 (ch), and 3. B x P. Mate.

PUZZLE No. 143

White	Black
1. R—KKt4	R x R*
2. B—KKt7	Any move
3. Mates according to Black's play	

*1.	P x P**
2. Q—KKt8 (ch)	K moves
3. Q x B. Mate	

**If 1. Kt—KB5, then White follows with 2. Kt—K3 (ch) and mate next move.

•

PUZZLE No. 144

White	Black
1. R—Q5 (ch)	P x R (best)
2. R—KKt7	B x R*
3. B—K7	B—KB1
4. B—QKt4 (ch)	B x B
5. P x B. Mate	

*2.	B—KB8
3. B—K7	B—QB5 (ch)
4. K—R3	Any move
5. B mates	

•

PUZZLE No. 145

White	Black
1. Kt—QP (dis ch)	K x Kt*
2. P—QB4	R x P**
3. Q—Q8 (ch)	R or B interposes
4. Q—KR4, or Q—KB6. Mate	

*If Black moves otherwise, he will be mated in three moves.

**Should Black play 2. Kt x P, White replies 3. Q—B4 (ch), and Q—K4 and mate. If Black plays 2. B x P (ch), then follows 3. B x B, and Q or B mates. And, finally, if 2. P—KB4, White answers with 3. Q—K3 (ch), and P x Kt and mate.

PUZZLE No. 146

White	Black
1. B—Q3	Q—KR6
2. Q—QB7 (ch)	K—Q4
3. R—Q4 (ch)	K x R, K—K3, or K—QB4
4. Q—Q6 or QR7. Mate	

•

PUZZLE No. 147

White	Black
1. Kt—Q5	Q x P (ch) (best)
2. Q x Q	K—Q5 (best)
3. B—QKt5	K—QB4*
4. P—QB4	Any move
5. Q mates	

*3.	P—Q3**
4. Q—K3 (ch)	K x Kt
5. P mates	

**If 3. K—K5, then follows 4. P—B3, and 5. Kt mates.

•

PUZZLE No. 148

White	Black
1. B—KR6 (ch)	Kt—KB5
2. B—QKt1	R—Q2, or any move
3. Kt x QBP (ch)	P x Kt
4. R—KR5	Q—K5 (best)
5. R—KR3 (ch)	Q interposes
6. R x Q. Mate	

•

PUZZLE No. 149

White	Black
1. Q—KR8	Q—QR3*
2. Q—Q8	Kt x Kt at KB3**
3. R—QB4 (ch)	Q x R, or K—Kt2
4. Q—QR8 or R x P. Mate	

*1.	R x P
2. R—QKt6 (ch)	P x R
3. Q—QB8 (ch)	K moves
4. Q x P. Mate	

**If Q—QB1, then follows R—QKt8 (ch), and mate next move. If Q—QKt4, then Q—QR8 (ch), and mate next move.

•

PUZZLE No. 150

White	Black
1. Kt—QKt 3 (ch)	Kt x Kt*
2. B x Kt	Kt—Q3 (best)
3. R—KKt7	Any move
4. R—KKt1. Mate	

*1.	R x Kt
2. B x R	Either Kt moves
3. R checks	Any move
4. R mates	

•

PUZZLE No. 151

White	Black
1. R x B	K x R*
2. Q—KR3	K—K4 or QB4, or P—QKt4**
3. Q x R	K or P moves
4. Q mates	

*1.	R—KKt6*** ****
2. K—KB7 (dis ch)	R—KKt2 (best)
3. Q x R (ch)	K moves
4. Q mates	

**If K—Q4 or K5, the mate is equally given by Q x R, etc.

***1.	K—K3*****
2. Q—K8 (ch)	K—KB4
3. Q—KKt6 (ch)	K moves
4. Q mates	

134

****If R—QB2 (ch), then follows K—Kt6 (dis ch), etc.

*****If K—KB4, White plays 2. Q—KR5 (ch), and gives mate next move.

•

PUZZLE No. 152

White	Black
1. B—KR5	Kt—QKt3*
2. Kt—K4	K—B4**
3. B—KKt6 (ch),	
and mate next move	

*1.	K—K4*** ****
2. Q—K7 (ch)	K—Q5*****
3. Kt—QKt5 (ch)	K moves
4. Q or B mates	

**If Black plays 2. P x Kt, or P—Q5, or Kt—Q2, White checks with B at KKt4, and mates next move.

***1.	K—KB3******
2. Kt—KB7	K—K3 (best)
3. Q—Q6 and mate next move	

****If Kt—QB4, then P x Kt and White mates obviously in two more moves.

*****If K—B5, White plays Kt—KB7, and gives mate next move.

******1.	P—Q5
2. Kt—QB4	K—Q4 (best)
3. B—KB3 (ch) and	
Q mates	

•

PUZZLE No. 153

White	Black
1. B—QB6 (ch)	K x Kt*
2. Kt—Q2	Kt x B** ***
3. Kt—K4 (ch)	K—K2 or
	Kt x Kt
4. Q mates	

*If Kt x B, then follows 2. Q—QB4 (ch), and 3. Q x Kt. Mate.

**2.	R x Kt
3. B—KKt7	Any move****
4. Q or B mates	

***If Black plays 2. B—KR2, the mate is given by 3. Kt—QB4 (ch), and 4. B—K7. If Black plays 2. Q—KR5, then R x Q, and Q or Kt mates. Finally, if 2. Q—K4, White plays 3. Q—QKt4 (ch), and mate next move.

****Editor's Note: I am unwilling to throw a doubt upon the integrity of this clever puzzle, but it does appear to me that in the last variation Black may avert the mate by now moving his King to QB4 and interposing the Rook at Q3 when White's Bishop gives check.

•

PUZZLE No. 154

White	Black
1. Q—K4	Q or R—QR5
2. Kt—KB2	Q or R x Q (ch)*
3. Kt x Q or R (ch)	K—K4 or K3
	(dis ch)
4. Kt—KKt5	K—Q4**
5. B—KB7. Mate	

*2.	Kt—K4
3. K—Kt3	Q or R x Q***
4. Kt x Q or R (ch)	K—K3
5. Kt—QB7. Mate	

**If Black plays 4. K—B5, then follows 5. R—K4. Mate. If 4. K—B3, then we have 5. Kt—R7. Mate.

***3.	B—Q3
4. Q—KB5 (ch)	K—K2
5. Q—KB7. Mate	

•

PUZZLE No. 155

White	Black
1. B x P	R—KR1*
2. R x P	R—K1 (best)
3. R—QR6	R moves
4. Kt—QB7 and	
R mates next move	

*1.	P—Q3
2. Kt—QKt6	R—R1 (best)
3. R x P	R—KKt1
4. R x QP. Mate	

•

PUZZLE No. 156

White	Black
1. B—KB6	B x B
2. Q—KR5	B—Q4
3. Q—R7 (ch)	K—B1
4. R—KB1	Any move
5. Q mates	

•

PUZZLE No. 157

White	Black
1. Kt—KB5	Kt x Kt (best)
2. Q—K5	P x Q
3. B—Kt5 (ch)	K—Q5
4. Kt—K6 (ch)	K x P
5. B mates	

•

PUZZLE No. 158

White	Black
1. Kt—QR7	B—Q7 (hest)
2. Q—KB8	B—KB5 (best)
3. Q—QR8. Mate	

•

PUZZLE No. 159

White	Black
1. P—Q6	P—K4*
2. Q—QR7	Any move
3. Q mates	

*1.	K—K4**
2. Q—QB1	Any move
3. Q mates	

**If K—KB5, White then plays 2. Q—QB5, and mate next move.

•

PUZZLE No. 160

White	Black
1. K—R3	Q x Q* **
2. P—Q4	Q x P***
3. Kt—Kt3 (ch)	K x Kt
4. R—KB5. Mate	

*1.	Q—KKt2
2. Q—Q4 (ch)	Q x Q
3. Kt—Kt3 (ch)	K x Kt
4. R—KB5. Mate	

If R x Q, then follows 2. P—Q3 (ch), etc.**

***If 2. P x P in passing, then ensues 3. Kt—Kt3 (ch), and mate next move. If 2. Kt—Q6, White replies with 3. Kt—Kt3 (ch), and mate next move.

****Editor's Note: All very well and good, but how is mate to be given in two moves if Black now plays R x P?

•

PUZZLE No. 161

White	Black
1. Q—KB7	K x Kt
2. K—QB2	P—QKt8
	(queens,
	giving ch)
3. R x Q	P—K8 (queens)
4. R x Q. Mate	

•

PUZZLE No. 162

White	Black
1. Kt—QB5*	B x R**
2. Q—K4	Any move
3. Q mates at KB4, K8, QKt7, or QR8	

*If White plays the more obvious move of R—K7, Black's reply is B—K3.

** 1.	P x P
2. Q x B (ch)	K—B2 or R2
3. P x P. Mate	

•

PUZZLE No. 163

White	Black
1. Q x QRP	P—QB4 (best)
2. Q—QR2	P x Q*
3. R—QKt2	Any move
4. R—KB2. Mate	

*2.	P—QKt7**
3. Q x P	Any move
4. Q—KB2 or B x KP. Mate	

**If R x Q, then follows R x Q (ch), and mate next move.

•

PUZZLE No. 164

White	Black
1. Q—KKt4	P x Q***
2. Kt—K5	Any move
3. Kt—Q3 or 7. Mate	

*1.	Kt—KB6
2. Q x P (ch)	Kt—K4
3. Q x Kt. Mate	

**If Black plays P—QKt6, then follows 2. Q x P (ch), 3. Q—QR5. Mate.

•

PUZZLE No. 165

White	Black
1. Kt—KKt7	Kt—QB4*
2. B—K6 (ch)	Kt x B
3. Kt—KB5	Any move
4. Kt mates at K3 or 7, or the other Kt mates at QB3 or 7	

*1.	B x KBP
2. B—K6	K moves
3. Kt—KB5	Any move
4. Kt—QB3. Mate	

•

PUZZLE No. 166

White	Black
1. Q—KKt3	P—K5
2. Q—K5	Any move
3. Q, B, or Kt mates	

•

PUZZLE No. 167

White	Black
1. P—QKt3	K x Kt (best)
2. Kt—Q2	P x Kt*
3. K—B5	P—B5
4. P—Kt4	P queens
5. P—K4. Mate	

*If Black reverses his second and third moves, White reverses his third and fourth, and the result is the same.

•

PUZZLE No. 168

White	Black
1. R—QKt3	K x P (best)*
2. Kt x P	K—QKt2 (best)
3. R—QKt5	K moves
4. B or Kt mates	

*If K x Kt, White plays either Kt—Q4 or Kt—QR7 (dis ch), etc.

•

PUZZLE No. 169

White	Black
1. Kt—QKt6	P x Kt*
2. P—QB7	B x P,
	or any move
3. R—Q8	K or B x R,
	or any move
4. Kt mates accordingly as Black plays	

*If the Bishop is moved, 2. White's Kt checks and Black's K moves, and 3. White's R mates.

•

PUZZLE No. 170

White	Black
1. Q—QKt3	R x B*
2. Kt—K7 (dbl ch)	K—R1**
3. Q—KKt6 (ch)	R x Q
4. Kt—KKt6 (ch)	P x Kt
5. R—KR3. Mate	

*If 1. P—KKt3, White replies with Kt—KB4 (ch), Q—KB7, etc. If 1. K—B1, then follows 2. Q—QKt4 (ch), 3. Kt—KB6 (ch), etc.

**If 2. K—B1, White plays 3. Q—K6.

•

PUZZLE No. 171

White	Black
1. Q—K4 (ch)	P x Q
2. B—Q7	P—K6*
3. Kt—KKt4	Any move
4. Kt—KB6, Mate	

*2.	P—KB6**
3. Kt—QB2	Any move
4. Kt mates at K3 or QKt4	

**If P—KKt4 or P—QR3 or QR4, White plays as in the former variation.

PUZZLE No. 172

White	Black
1. Kt—K4	Kt x Kt (best)*
2. B—QB2	P—KKt6
3. B—QKt1	Kt moves
4. P—KKt7. Mate	

*1.	Kt—KR4
2. Kt—KKt5	Any move
3. P mates	

•

PUZZLE No. 173

White	Black
1. R x KKtP	R x R*
2. Kt—KKt7	Any move
3. R or Kt mates	

*If R—Q6, then follows 2. Kt—Q4, etc. Again, if R x QP (ch), White answers with Kt x R, etc.

•

PUZZLE No. 174

White	Black
1. R—QB1	Kt—K5*
2. Q—QKt3	Any move
3. PQ or Kt mates	

| *1. | B—K4 |
| 2. R—Q1 (ch), and mates next move | |

•

PUZZLE No. 175

White	Black
1. Kt—KKt7	B x Q*
2. Kt—KB5	R—KKt2**
3. Kt—K3 (ch)	K moves
4. B mates	

*1.	P—K3
2. Kt—KB5	P x Kt
3. R x B (ch), and Q mates	

**If Kt—KB5, White answers with 2.
Q—B6 (ch), 3. Kt x RP, and mate
next move.

•

PUZZLE No. 176

WHITE	BLACK
1. B—KKt6	B—KKt5*
2. B—K8	Q—K2 or
	B—KB6**
3. Q x QBP	Kt—QB7 (best)
4. Q—QR4 (ch)	P x Q
5. Kt mates	

*If Black plays B—KB4, then follows
2. Kt x P (ch), 3. Q—Q1 (ch), and
mate in two more moves.

**2.	Q or B x R
3. B—QKt6 (ch)	K x B
4. Q—QB6 (ch)	Kt—QR4
5. Q mates	

•

PUZZLE No. 177

WHITE	BLACK
1. Kt—QR8	P x P (best)
2. Kt—QKt6	P x Q (best)
3. Kt—K1 (ch)	K—K6
4. Kt x QP. Mate	

•

PUZZLE No. 178

WHITE	BLACK
1. Kt—KB6	Kt x Kt*
2. R—Q7 (ch)	Kt x R (best)
3. P—KB6	Any move
4. Kt or B mates	

*1.	R—Q1
2. Kt—KKt4	R—Q3, or
	Kt—K3,
	or Kt—QB4
3. B—QKt6, and	
mates next move	
accordingly	

PUZZLE No. 179

WHITE	BLACK
1. R x KKtP	P x R (dis ch)*
2. R—KR7 (dis ch)	K moves
3. B mates	

*1.	K—Q5**
2. R—Q7 (dbl ch)	K moves
3. R—KKt4. Mate	

**If Black plays 1. P—QR4, then
follows R—QR7 (dis ch), and mate
next move.

Note: Should White at his first move
play R—KKt5, Black answers with
P—K4, etc.

•

PUZZLE No. 180

WHITE	BLACK
1. R—KKt3	K—B5*
2. Q—Q3	P x Q
3. B—QB6 and mate	
next move	

*1.	P—K4**
2. B—KKt5	Any move
White mates	
obviously	
in two moves	

**If Black plays 1. Kt—QB6, then
White answers with 2. B x P (ch) and
mates in two more moves. Again, if
Black plays 1. R—Q2, the reply is 2.
Q—KKt8, 3. Q—Kt5 (ch), 4. Q x P.
Mate.

•

PUZZLE No. 181

WHITE	BLACK
1. Q—QKt6	R—QB4 (best)*
2. Q—QBP	Either R x Q
3. Kt—K8	Any move
4. Kt mates	

*If Black plays P x Q, White plays
K—K8 and then gives mate.

139

Note: It is noticeable in this problem that, if White at his second move takes the Rook on Black's QB4, Black moves the Kt from QR8 to QB7, etc. Again, if White at move 2 plays Q—Q6, instead of taking the QB Pawn, Black replies with Kt—KB6 or P—KB3.

•

PUZZLE No. 182

WHITE	BLACK
1. Kt—KB1 (ch)	K—K7*
2. Q—Q6**	R—Q6 (best)
3. Kt—K6	R—KB1
4. Q x R (ch)	B x Q
5. Kt mates	

*If either P x Q, the Kt is played to K6, and mate follows next move.

**If White, for the second move, plays Kt—K6 instead of Q—Q6, Black answers with P—QB4, and, on the White Q taking QBP, Black checks with his Queen, etc.

•

PUZZLE No. 183

WHITE	BLACK
1. B x QBP	P x B (best)
2. R—QKt2	K—Q4*
3. Q x P (ch)	K x Q**
4. Kt—QKt6. Mate	

*If B x Kt, White's Q x P, checking, and mates next move. Again, if Black at move 2 plays Kt—Q7, White's R x Kt, and mate follows next move.

**If K—QB3, White plays Kt—QKt8, checkmate.

PUZZLE No. 184

WHITE	BLACK
1. Kt x P	Kt x P (best)*
2. Kt—Q5	K—QB4**
3. Q—QKt1	Any move
4. Q mates	

*If B x P, then White plays Kt—Q5 or QR4.

**2.	K—K7.
3. Q—QB1	Any move
4. QR or Kt gives mate	

•

PUZZLE No. 185

WHITE	BLACK
1. R—QKt5	P—QB4*
2. B—QR8	B x B (best)
3. R—QKt1 and mate next move	

*If B x B, then White plays 2. R x B, 3. R x KKtP, 4. R mates. If P—QB3, White plays 2. B x B (ch), 3. R x KKtP, etc.

•

PUZZLE No. 186

WHITE	BLACK
1. B—KKt4	P—KR3 or KR4
2. B—Q1	P—KR4 or KR5*
3. B—QR4	P moves**
4. Kt—Q3	K moves
5. R mates	

*Or any other move except playing the King.

**3.	K—Q3
4. K—Q4	Any move
5. R mates	

•

PUZZLE No. 187

White	Black
1. Q—QR8	R x Q
2. B—QKt4	R—Q1 (ch)
3. Kt—Q7. Dbl ch and mate	

•

PUZZLE No. 188

White	Black
1. Kt—Q6 (ch)	K—K3
2. Kt—KB3	B x P (best)
3. P x B	Q—KKt8 (best)
4. K—Q8	Any move
5. BKt or P mates	

•

PUZZLE No. 189

White	Black
1. R—QKt4	P—R7*
2. Q—K3 (ch)	P x Q
3. Kt—K5 (dis ch)	

*1.	K—Q6
2. K—Q5	Any move
3. Q mates	

•

PUZZLE No. 190

White	Black
1. B—KB5	K—KB3
2. R—QR1	K—Kt4*
3. Kt—K4 (ch)	K moves
4. B mates	

*2.	K—K2
3. R—QR7 (ch)	K moves
4. R or Kt mates	

•

PUZZLE No. 191

White	Black
1. Kt x KRP	K—QB5*
2. R—Q5	K x R (best)
3. Kt from R3—KB4 (ch)	K moves
4. B or Kt mates	

*1.	K—Q3
2. R—Q5 (ch)	P or B x R**
3. B—K5 (ch)	K moves
4. Kt mates	

*If K x R, then follows 3. Kt—KB4 (ch), and 4. B—K5. Mate.

•

PUZZLE No. 192

White	Black
1. Q—QKt3	B—Q4 (best)
2. Q—Q1	P—KB5
3. Q—KR5	Kt—Q2
4. Q—K5 (ch)	Kt x Q
5. Kt mates	

•

PUZZLE No. 193

White	Black
1. Q—QR1	K—KB5 (best)
2. Q—QR6	K—Kt4, K4, or B6
3. Q mates	

•

PUZZLE No. 194

White	Black
1. B—KR8	K—QR2*
2. Q—QR1	K—QKt2
3. Q—KKt7. Mate	

*1.	K—QB2
2. Q—QB2 (ch)	K moves
3. Q—QB6. Mate	

•

PUZZLE No. 195

White	Black
1. R—Q5 (ch)	K—K5*
2. Kt—KB3	K x Kt**
3. R—Q2, dis mate	

*If 1. K—K3, White still plays 2. Kt—KB3 and mates next move.

**If Black plays any other move, then follows 3. Kt—Q2 mate, or 3. Kt x KKtP mate.

•

PUZZLE No. 196

White	Black
1. B—Q4	K moves*
2. K—Q5	K—QB2
3. K—K6	Any move
4. R—QB8. Mate	

*1.	Kt—KR6**
2. K—Q5	Kt checks
3. K—QB6	Any move
4. R—K8. Mate	

**If Black moves one of the Pawns, then follows 2. R—KR7 (ch), 3. K—K6 and mate next move.

•

PUZZLE No. 197

White	Black
1. B—K1	B—B4*
2. B—QB3 (ch)	Any move
3. Q mates	

*1.	K x R**
2. Q—KKt3 (ch) and mate next move	

**If Black plays 1. K—QB4, then follows 2. Q—QB7 (ch), and mate next move.

•

PUZZLE No. 198

White	Black
1. Q—KKt1	P—QKt4*
2. B—QB3 (ch)	K x B**
3. Q—Q4. Mate	

*If Black plays 1. P—QR8 and claims a Queen or other piece, White replies with 2. B—QB3 (ch), and mate next move.

**If 2. K—QR6, White plays 3. Q—QR7. Mate.

•

PUZZLE No. 199

White	Black
1. B—QKt4	B—Q4*
2. Q—K6	Any move
3. Q or Kt mates	

*If 1. Kt—Q4, White replies with 2. Q—KB5, etc.

•

PUZZLE No. 200

White	Black
1. Kt—Q3	P x Kt (best)
2. B—QB3	Q x QB tbest)
3. R x KKtP	Q—QB4 or QB5
4. P—QB4 dis checkmate	

•

142

INDEX

References are to puzzle number and not to page